K-A

TEACHER GUIDE

Ready® | K Mathematics
PRACTICE AND
PROBLEM SOLVING
Teacher Guide

Program Authors

Mark Ellis, Ph.D.
Department Chair and Professor, Education, CSU Fullerton
Board of Directors, Executive Committee, NCTM
National Board Certified Teacher

Gladis Kersaint, Ph.D.
Professor, Mathematics Education, USF
Board of Directors, Executive Committee, NCTM
Board of Directors, Association of Mathematics Teacher Educators

Acknowledgments

Vice President–Product Development: Adam Berkin
Editorial Director: Cynthia Tripp
Editors: Pamela Halloran, Djana Paper, Susan Rogalski
Project Manager: Grace Izzi
Cover Design: Matt Pollock
Book Designer: Scott Hoffman

ISBN 978-1-4957-1679-9
©2016—Curriculum Associates, LLC
North Billerica, MA 01862

Table of Contents

Mathematics Lessons

Student Book includes a Family Letter for every lesson.

Mathematics Lessons *continued*

Student Book includes a Family Letter for every lesson.

Mathematics Lessons *continued*

Student Book includes a Family Letter for every lesson.

Mathematics Lessons *continued*

		Standards	Embedded SMPs

Student Book includes a Family Letter for every lesson.

Mathematics Lessons *continued*

Teacher Resource Blackline Masters

Teacher Resource blackline masters are provided for use with lesson practice and collaborative practice games in *Ready Practice and Problem Solving*.

- See the Teacher Resources Table of Contents on page 131 for lessons requiring a blackline master.
- See the Unit Game Step by Step for full instructions for use of blackline masters with the Unit Games.

Student Book includes a Family Letter for every lesson.

Ready® Program Overview

Ready Mathematics prepares students for mastery of rigorous national and state standards through a balance of conceptual understanding, procedural skills, fluency, and application. Use *Ready's* clear, thoughtful pedagogy to support rich classroom instruction in which meaningful reasoning, mathematical discourse, and a range of mathematical practices thrive.

Built for the new standards. Not just aligned.

For Students

Ready Instruction provides whole class and small group instruction and independent practice of concepts and skills for every standard. Unit Reviews give frequent opportunities for standards mastery monitoring.

Ready Practice and Problem Solving complements ***Ready Instruction*** through rich practice and games that develop understanding of and fluency with key skills and concepts.

For Teachers

The ***Ready Teacher Resource Book*** and ***Ready Practice and Problem Solving Teacher Guide*** support teachers with point-of-use strategies and tips, step-by-step guidance, and best practices for implementing rigorous standards.

Ready Teacher Toolbox provides online access to prerequisite lessons from previous grades, student-led center activities differentiated for three levels, and teacher-led activities for students requiring additional instruction on prerequisite or on-level skills.

Ready Program Features

 Built with **all-new content** written specifically for rigorous national and state standards

 Uses a research-based, **gradual release** instructional model

 Requires **higher-order thinking** and complex reasoning to solve problems

 Integrates **Standards for Mathematical Practice** throughout every lesson

 Embeds thoughtful **teacher support**

 Encourages students to develop **deeper understanding** of concepts and to understand and use a variety of mathematical strategies and models

 Promotes **fluency** and connects hands-on learning with clearly articulated models throughout

What's in *Ready® Practice and Problem Solving*

Building on *Ready Instruction*, **Ready Practice and Problem Solving** encourages students to reason, use strategies, solve extended problems, and engage in collaborative work to extend classroom learning. Designed for flexibility, **Ready Practice and Problem Solving** can be used for homework, independent classroom practice, and in after-school settings.

Lesson Features

Family Letters, one for each lesson, serve as a home-school connection to support student learning. Family Letters can be sent home separately before each lesson, or as part of a family communication package. Practice specific to each part of every *Ready Instruction* lesson gives students multiple opportunities to reinforce procedural fluency and synthesize concepts and skills learned in the classroom. Lesson practice can be used at the end of a lesson or after completing each part of a lesson.

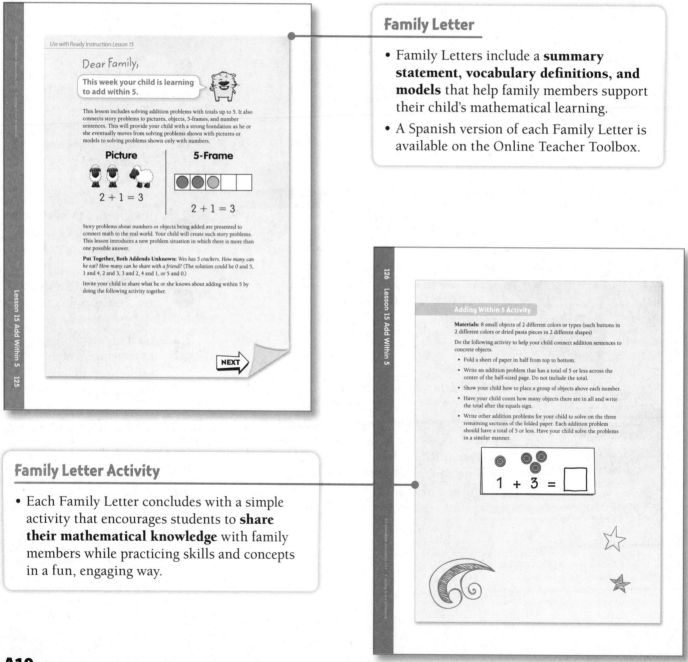

Family Letter

- Family Letters include a **summary statement, vocabulary definitions, and models** that help family members support their child's mathematical learning.

- A Spanish version of each Family Letter is available on the Online Teacher Toolbox.

Family Letter Activity

- Each Family Letter concludes with a simple activity that encourages students to **share their mathematical knowledge** with family members while practicing skills and concepts in a fun, engaging way.

A10

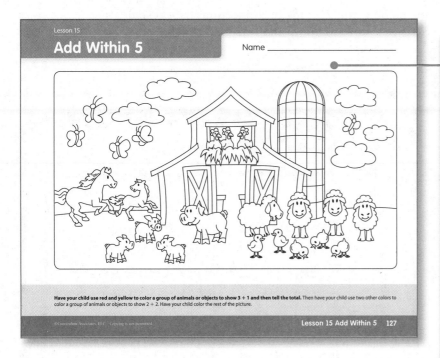

Add Within 5

Name _____

Have your child use red and yellow to color a group of animals or objects to show 3 + 1 and then tell the total. Then have your child use two other colors to color a group of animals or objects to show 2 + 2. Have your child color the rest of the picture.

Skills and Concepts Practice

- **Two pages of skills and concept practice** are provided after each Modeled Instruction section, each Guided Exploration section, and each Guided Practice section of a *Ready Instruction* lesson. These can be used in class, after school, or at home.

- The opening situation is an opportunity for students to personalize the mathematics of the lesson. These situations have multiple points of entry and/or more than one correct answer, providing experience in independent critical thinking and problem solving for all learners.

- **Scaffolded examples** support and reinforce students' classroom learning.

- Students are encouraged to show their work and **use models and strategies** they learned in the *Ready Instruction* lesson.

- Problems are **differentiated** to provide maximum flexibility when assigning practice as independent classwork or homework. The differentiation is marked in the Teacher Guide as basic **B**, medium **M**, or challenge **C**.

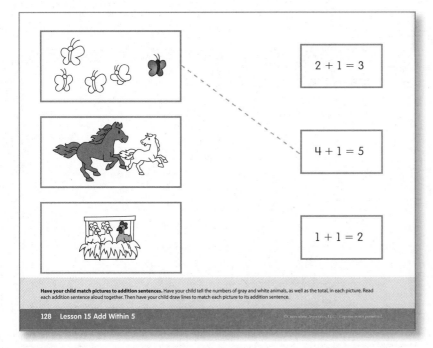

2 + 1 = 3

4 + 1 = 5

1 + 1 = 2

Have your child match pictures to addition sentences. Have your child tell the numbers of gray and white animals, as well as the total, in each picture. Read each addition sentence aloud together. Then have your child draw lines to match each picture to its addition sentence.

Unit Features

Unit materials cover multiple skills and concepts, helping students make connections across standards. Use Unit Games and Unit Practice after completing each unit to apply and integrate skills and to consolidate learning.

Unit Game

- Unit Games are engaging, collaborative experiences designed to encourage students to use **mathematical reasoning** as they play with a partner.

- Students record the mathematics of each game to **promote fluency** and reinforce learning. The recording sheet also serves as an opportunity for informal assessment to monitor students' work.

- These partner games can be used at classroom centers and/or sent home for play with a family member.

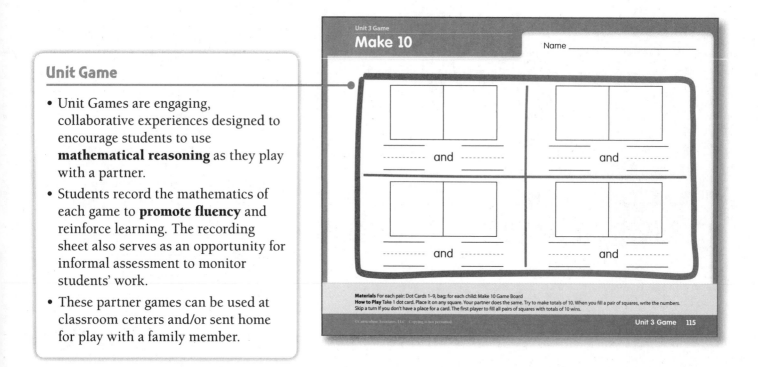

Unit 3 Game
Make 10
Name _____

___ and ___   ___ and ___

___ and ___   ___ and ___

Materials For each pair: Dot Cards 1–9, bag; for each child: Make 10 Game Board
How to Play Take 1 dot card. Place it on any square. Your partner does the same. Try to make totals of 10. When you fill a pair of squares, write the numbers. Skip a turn if you don't have a place for a card. The first player to fill all pairs of squares with totals of 10 wins.

©Curriculum Associates, LLC   Copying is not permitted.   Unit 3 Game   115

Unit Practice

- The Unit Practice provides **mixed practice** of lesson skills and concepts.

- Each Unit Practice **integrates multiple skills** and helps students develop critical thinking skills by including problems with more than one answer or problems that can be solved with various strategies.

- The unit practice pages can be assigned as homework, used as independent or small group practice, or used for whole class discussion.

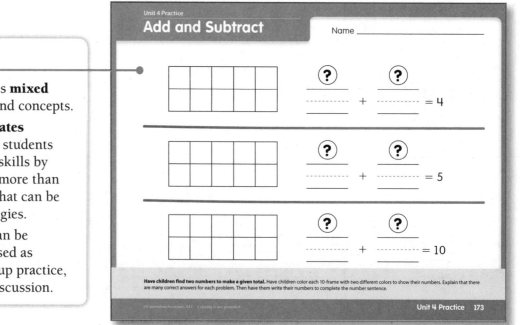

Unit 4 Practice
Add and Subtract
Name _____

(?)   (?)
___ + ___ = 4

(?)   (?)
___ + ___ = 5

(?)   (?)
___ + ___ = 10

Have children find two numbers to make a given total. Have children color each 10-frame with two different colors to show their numbers. Explain that there are many correct answers for each problem. Then have them write their numbers to complete the number sentence.

©Curriculum Associates, LLC   Copying is not permitted.   Unit 4 Practice   173

Fluency Practice

Throughout instruction, use Fluency Skills and Fluency Repeated Reasoning worksheets to reinforce procedural fluency.

Skills Practice

- Fluency practice worksheets in multiple formats provide flexibility and promote the **use of grade-appropriate strategies and algorithms**.
- These worksheets address grade-level facts and operations and can be used any time after the skill has been taught.

Repeated Reasoning

- Repeated Reasoning worksheets encourage students to **make use of structure and look for regularity** as part of their development of grade-level fluency.
- In this type of fluency practice, students identify and talk about patterns in the relationship between the answers and the problems. This develops their **abstract reasoning** and mental math skills.

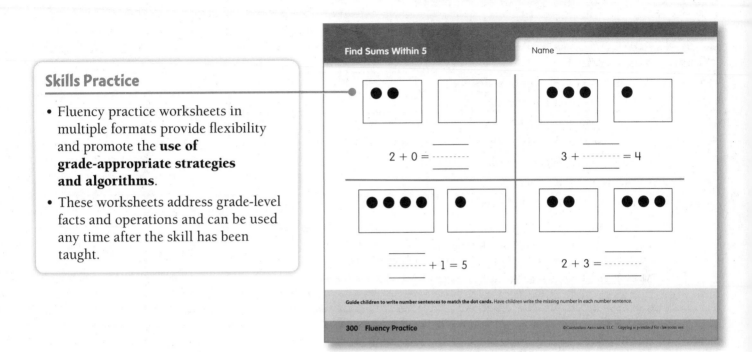

Correlations

Common Core Standards in *Ready® Practice and Problem Solving*

The tables below show the standards addressed in **Ready Practice and Problem Solving**, all of which correspond to **Ready Instruction**. Use this information to plan and focus meaningful practice.

Common Core State Standards for Kindergarten — Mathematics Standards		Content Emphasis	Ready® Practice and Problem Solving Lesson(s)
Counting and Cardinality			
Know number names and the count sequence.			
K.CC.A.1	Count to 100 by ones and by tens.	Major	24, 25
K.CC.A.2	Count forward beginning from a given number within the known sequence (instead of having to begin at 1).	Major	24, 25
K.CC.A.3	Write numbers from 0 to 20. Represent a number of objects with a written numeral 0–20 (with 0 representing a count of no objects).	Major	2, 3, 4, 7, 9, 11, 22
Count to tell the number of objects.			
K.CC.B.4	Understand the relationship between numbers and quantities; connect counting to cardinality.	Major	1, 2, 3, 4, 5, 7, 9, 11, 12
K.CC.B.4a	When counting objects, say the number names in the standard order, pairing each object with one and only one number name and each number name with one and only one object.	Major	1, 2, 3, 4, 7, 9, 11
K.CC.B.4b	Understand that the last number name said tells the number of objects counted. The number of objects is the same regardless of their arrangement or the order in which they were counted.	Major	1, 2, 3, 4, 7, 9, 11
K.CC.B.4c	Understand that each successive number name refers to a quantity that is one larger.	Major	5, 12
K.CC.B.5	Count to answer "how many?" questions about as many as 20 things arranged in a line, a rectangular array, or a circle, or as many as 10 things in a scattered configuration; given a number from 1–20, count out that many objects.	Major	2, 3, 4, 7, 9, 11, 22
Compare numbers.			
K.CC.C.6	Identify whether the number of objects in one group is greater than, less than, or equal to the number of objects in another group, e.g., by using matching and counting strategies.	Major	5, 12
K.CC.C.7	Compare two numbers between 1 and 10 presented as written numerals.	Major	5, 12
Operations and Algebraic Thinking			
Understand addition as putting together and adding to, and understand subtraction as taking apart and taking from.			
K.OA.A.1	Represent addition and subtraction with objects, fingers, mental images, drawings, sounds (e.g., claps), acting out situations, verbal explanations, expressions, or equations.	Major	14, 16
K.OA.A.2	Solve addition and subtraction word problems, and add and subtract within 10, e.g., by using objects or drawings to represent the problem.	Major	15, 17, 18, 19
K.OA.A.3	Decompose numbers less than or equal to 10 into pairs in more than one way, e.g., by using objects or drawings, and record each decomposition by a drawing or equation (e.g., $5 = 2 + 3$ and $5 = 4 + 1$).	Major	6, 8, 10, 13
K.OA.A.4	For any number from 1 to 9, find the number that makes 10 when added to the given number, e.g., by using objects or drawings, and record the answer with a drawing or equation.	Major	13
K.OA.A.5	Fluently add and subtract within 5.	Major	6, 15, 17, 20

The Standards for Mathematical Practice are integrated throughout the lessons, unit practices, and unit games.

Common Core State Standards © 2010. National Governors Association Center for Best Practices and Council of Chief State School Officers. All rights reserved.

Common Core State Standards for Kindergarten — Mathematics Standards	Content Emphasis	*Ready* Practice and Problem Solving Lesson(s)
Number and Operations in Base Ten		
Work with numbers 11–19 to gain foundations for place value.		
K.NBT.A.1 Compose and decompose numbers from 11 to 19 into ten ones and some further ones, e.g., by using objects or drawings, and record each composition or decomposition by a drawing or equation (such as $18 = 10 + 8$); understand that these numbers are composed of ten ones and one, two, three, four, five, six, seven, eight, or nine ones.	Major	21, 23
Measurement and Data		
Describe and compare measurable attributes.		
K.MD.A.1 Describe measurable attributes of objects, such as length or weight. Describe several measurable attributes of a single object.	Supporting/ Additional	26, 27
K.MD.A.2 Directly compare two objects with a measurable attribute in common, to see which object has "more of"/"less of" the attribute, and describe the difference. *For example, directly compare the heights of two children and describe one child as taller/shorter.*	Supporting/ Additional	26, 27
Classify objects and count the number of objects in each category.		
K.MD.B.3 Classify objects into given categories; count the numbers of objects in each category and sort the categories by count.	Supporting/ Additional	28
Geometry		
Identify and describe shapes (squares, circles, triangles, rectangles, hexagons, cubes, cones, cylinders, and spheres).		
K.G.A.1 Describe objects in the environment using names of shapes, and describe the relative positions of these objects using terms such as *above, below, beside, in front of, behind,* and *next to.*	Supporting/ Additional	29
K.G.A.2 Correctly name shapes regardless of their orientations or overall size.	Supporting/ Additional	30
K.G.A.3 Identify shapes as two-dimensional (lying in a plane, "flat") or three-dimensional ("solid").	Supporting/ Additional	30
Analyze, compare, create, and compose shapes.		
K.G.B.4 Analyze and compare two- and three-dimensional shapes, in different sizes and orientations, using informal language to describe their similarities, differences, parts (e.g., number of sides and vertices/"corners") and other attributes (e.g., having sides of equal length).	Supporting/ Additional	31
K.G.B.5 Model shapes in the world by building shapes from components (e.g., sticks and clay balls) and drawing shapes.	Supporting/ Additional	32
K.G.B.6 Compose simple shapes to form larger shapes. *For example, "Can you join these two triangles with full sides touching to make a rectangle?"*	Supporting/ Additional	32

A15

Unit Correlations	
Unit	**Common Core State Standards**
Unit 1	
Unit Practice	K.CC.A.3, K.CC.B.4a, K.CC.B.4b, K.CC.B.5, K.OA.A.3, K.OA.A.5
Game: Roll and Count	K.CC.A.3, K.CC.B.4
Unit 2	
Unit Practice	K.CC.A.3, K.CC.B.4a, K.CC.B.4b, K.CC.B.5, K.OA.A.3
Game: Match 6, 7, 8, 9	K.CC.A.3, K.CC.B.4a, K.CC.B.4b, K.CC.B.5, K.OA.A.3
Unit 3	
Unit Practice	K.CC.B.4c, K.CC.C.6, K.CC.C.7, K.OA.A.3, K.OA.A.4
Game: Make 10	K.CC.A.3, K.CC.B.4a, K.CC.B.4b, K.CC.B.5, K.CC.C.6, K.OA.A.3, K.OA.A.4
Unit 4	
Unit Practice	K.OA.A.1, K.OA.A.2, K.OA.A.5
Game: Last One Wins	K.OA.A.1
Unit 5	
Unit Practice	K.CC.A.1, K.CC.A.2, K.NBT.A.1
Game: Teen Number Cover-Up	K.CC.A.3, K.NBT.A.1
Unit 6	
Unit Practice	K.MD.A.1, K.MD.A.2, K.MD.B.3
Game: Shorter and Longer	K.MD.A.1, K.MD.A.2
Unit 7	
Unit Practice	K.G.B.4, K.G.B.5, K.G.B.6
Game: Shape Cover-Up	K.G.A.3, K.G.B.4

You may wish to assign the following pages for practice after completing the Modeled Instruction in *Ready Mathematics.*

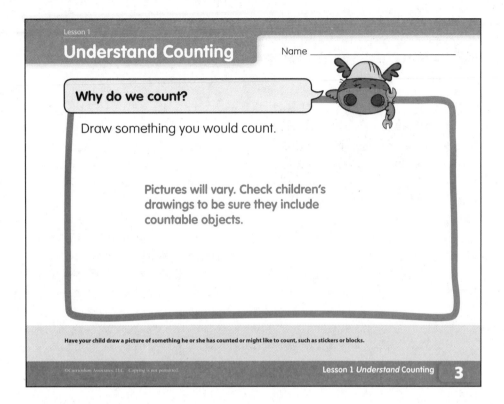

You may wish to assign the following pages for practice after completing the Guided Exploration in *Ready Mathematics*.

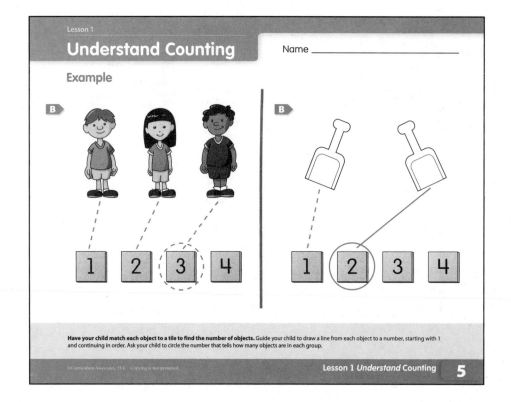

Lesson 1

Understand Counting

Name _____

Example

Have your child match each object to a tile to find the number of objects. Guide your child to draw a line from each object to a number, starting with 1 and continuing in order. Ask your child to circle the number that tells how many objects are in each group.

©Curriculum Associates, LLC   Copying is not permitted.

Lesson 1 *Understand* Counting   **5**

Key
B Basic
M Medium
C Challenge

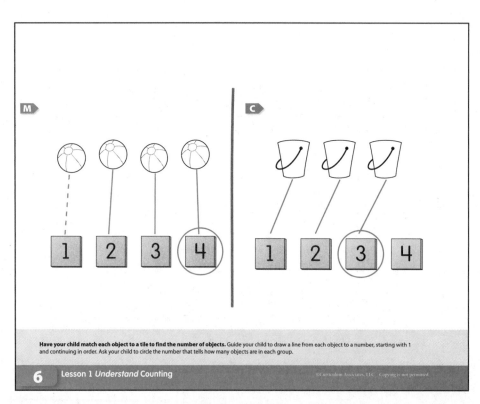

Have your child match each object to a tile to find the number of objects. Guide your child to draw a line from each object to a number, starting with 1 and continuing in order. Ask your child to circle the number that tells how many objects are in each group.

6   Lesson 1 *Understand* Counting   ©Curriculum Associates, LLC   Copying is not permitted.

You may wish to assign the following pages for practice after completing the Guided Practice in **Ready Mathematics.**

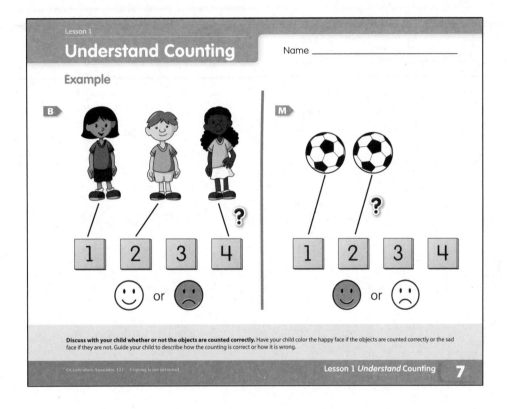

Lesson 1

Understand Counting

Name _____

Example

Discuss with your child whether or not the objects are counted correctly. Have your child color the happy face if the objects are counted correctly or the sad face if they are not. Guide your child to describe how the counting is correct or how it is wrong.

©Curriculum Associates, LLC Copying is not permitted.

Lesson 1 *Understand* Counting   **7**

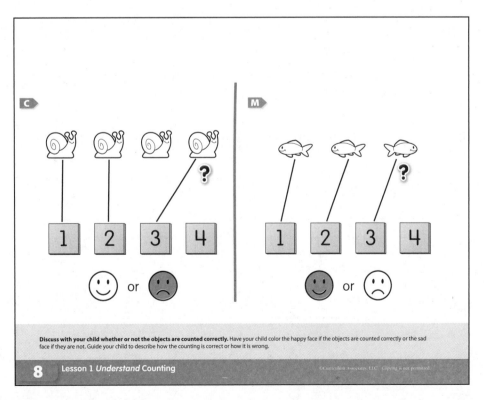

Discuss with your child whether or not the objects are counted correctly. Have your child color the happy face if the objects are counted correctly or the sad face if they are not. Guide your child to describe how the counting is correct or how it is wrong.

8   Lesson 1 *Understand* Counting

©Curriculum Associates, LLC Copying is not permitted.

You may wish to assign the following pages for practice after completing the Modeled Instruction in *Ready Mathematics*.

Lesson 2

Count 1, 2, and 3

Coloring will vary. Check to see that children have used a different color for each number of objects. Children should have colored groups of 1, 2, and 3 objects.

Have your child color groups of 1, 2, and 3 objects. Use a different color for each number. Then have your child color the rest of the picture.

©Curriculum Associates, LLC   Copying is not permitted.   Lesson 2 Count 1, 2, and 3   **11**

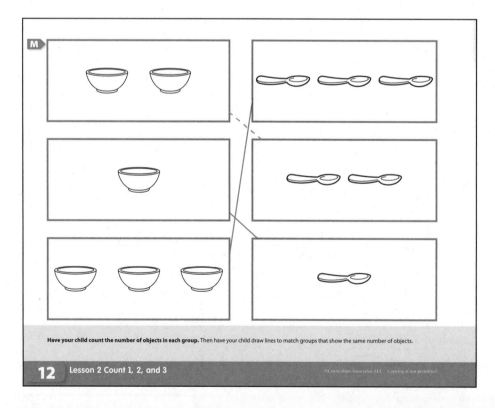

Have your child count the number of objects in each group. Then have your child draw lines to match groups that show the same number of objects.

12   Lesson 2 Count 1, 2, and 3   ©Curriculum Associates, LLC   Copying is not permitted.

You may wish to assign the following pages for practice after completing the first Guided Practice in *Ready Mathematics*.

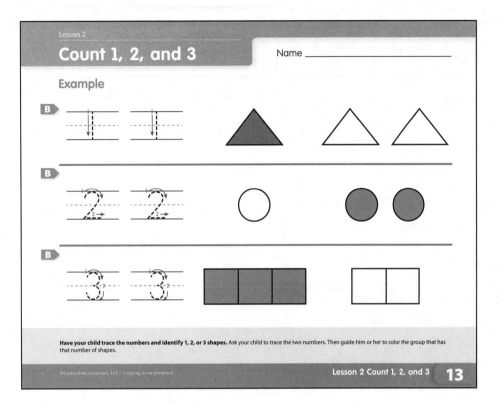

Lesson 2

Count 1, 2, and 3

Name _____

Example

Have your child trace the numbers and identify 1, 2, or 3 shapes. Ask your child to trace the two numbers. Then guide him or her to color the group that has that number of shapes.

©Curriculum Associates, LLC   Copying is not permitted.

Lesson 2 Count 1, 2, and 3   **13**

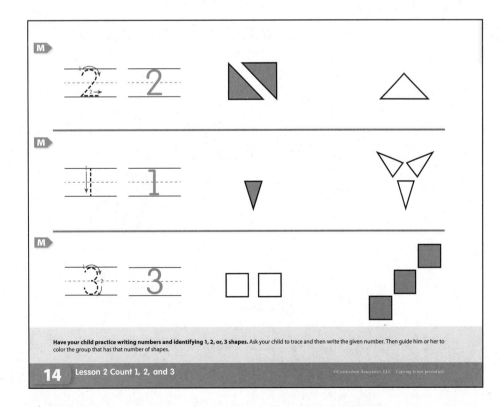

Have your child practice writing numbers and identifying 1, 2, or 3 shapes. Ask your child to trace and then write the given number. Then guide him or her to color the group that has that number of shapes.

14   Lesson 2 Count 1, 2, and 3

©Curriculum Associates, LLC   Copying is not permitted.

Key
B Basic
M Medium
C Challenge

You may wish to assign the following pages for practice after completing the second Guided Practice in *Ready Mathematics*.

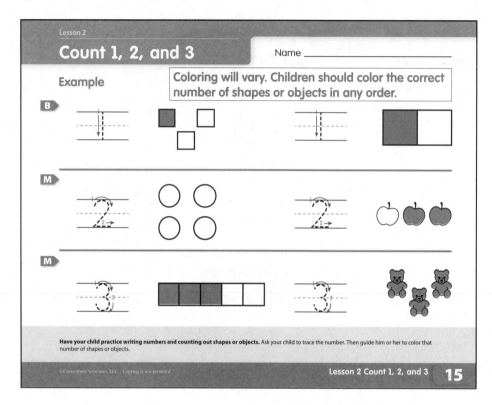

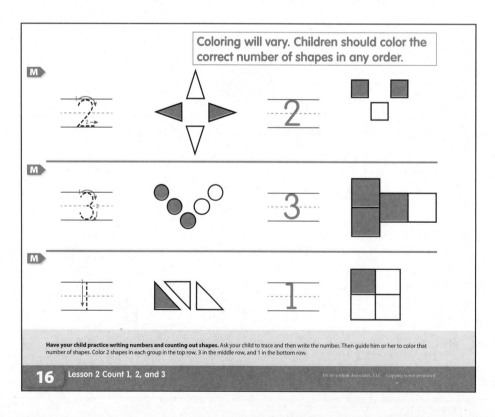

You may wish to assign the following pages for practice after completing the Modeled Instruction in *Ready Mathematics.*

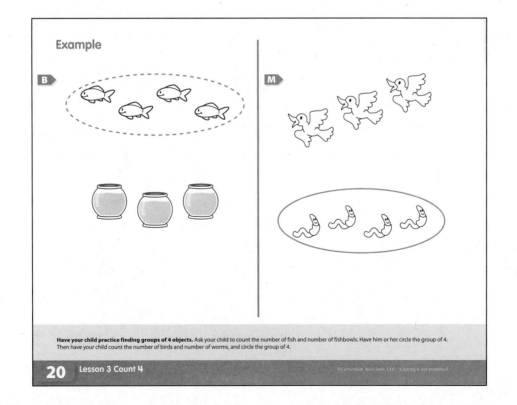

Lesson 3

Count 4

Check that children have colored groups of 4 similar objects red.

Have your child color groups of 4 similar objects red. Then have your child color the rest of the picture using different colors.

©Curriculum Associates, LLC   Copying is not permitted.

Lesson 3 Count 4 **19**

Example

B

M

Have your child practice finding groups of 4 objects. Ask your child to count the number of fish and number of fishbowls. Have him or her circle the group of 4. Then have your child count the number of birds and number of worms, and circle the group of 4.

20 Lesson 3 Count 4

©Curriculum Associates, LLC   Copying is not permitted.

You may wish to assign the following pages for practice after completing the first Guided Practice in *Ready Mathematics.*

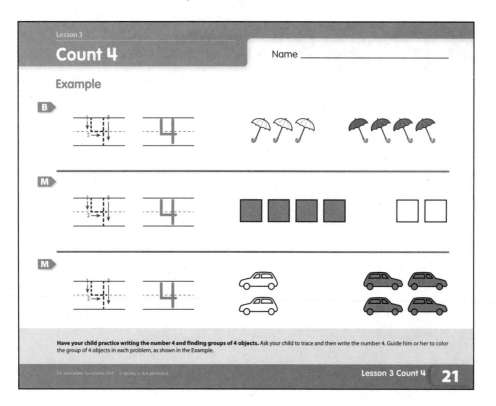

Lesson 3

Count 4   Name _____

Example

Have your child practice writing the number 4 and finding groups of 4 objects. Ask your child to trace and then write the number 4. Guide him or her to color the group of 4 objects in each problem, as shown in the Example.

©Curriculum Associates, LLC   Copying is not permitted.   Lesson 3 Count 4   **21**

Key

B Basic

M Medium

C Challenge

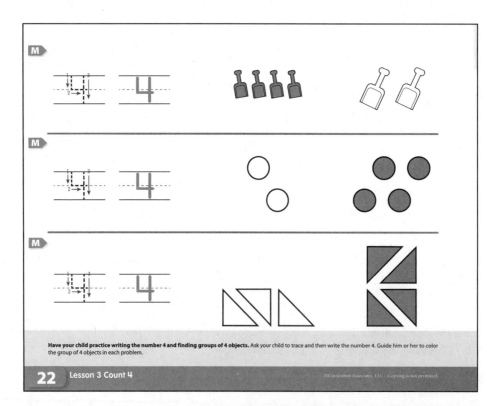

Have your child practice writing the number 4 and finding groups of 4 objects. Ask your child to trace and then write the number 4. Guide him or her to color the group of 4 objects in each problem.

22   Lesson 3 Count 4   ©Curriculum Associates, LLC   Copying is not permitted.

You may wish to assign the following pages for practice after completing the second Guided Practice in *Ready Mathematics*.

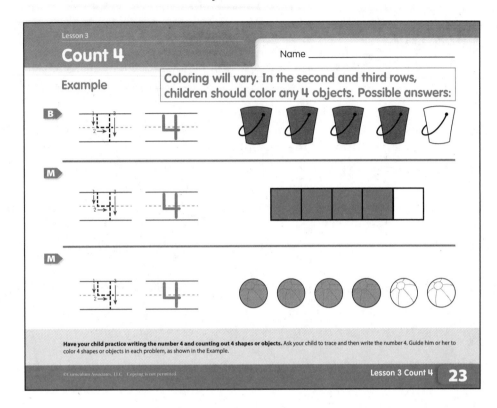

Lesson 3

Count 4

Name _____

Example

B Coloring will vary. In the second and third rows, children should color any 4 objects. Possible answers:

M

M

Have your child practice writing the number 4 and counting out 4 shapes or objects. Ask your child to trace and then write the number 4. Guide him or her to color 4 shapes or objects in each problem, as shown in the Example.

©Curriculum Associates, LLC   Copying is not permitted.   Lesson 3 Count 4   **23**

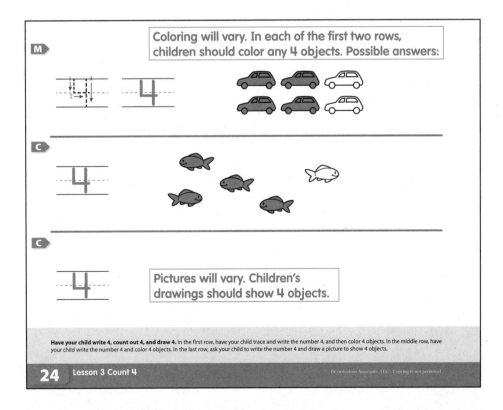

M Coloring will vary. In each of the first two rows, children should color any 4 objects. Possible answers:

C

C Pictures will vary. Children's drawings should show 4 objects.

Have your child write 4, count out 4, and draw 4. In the first row, have your child trace and write the number 4, and then color 4 objects. In the middle row, have your child write the number 4 and color 4 objects. In the last row, ask your child to write the number 4 and draw a picture to show 4 objects.

24   Lesson 3 Count 4   ©Curriculum Associates, LLC   Copying is not permitted.

You may wish to assign the following pages for practice after completing the Modeled Instruction in *Ready Mathematics*.

Lesson 4

Count 5

Check that children have colored groups of 5 similar objects blue. They should have also circled the number 5.

Have your child color groups of 5 similar objects blue. Then ask your child to color the rest of the picture using different colors. Finally, have your child circle the number 5 in the picture.

©Curriculum Associates, LLC · Copying is not permitted.   Lesson 4 Count 5   **27**

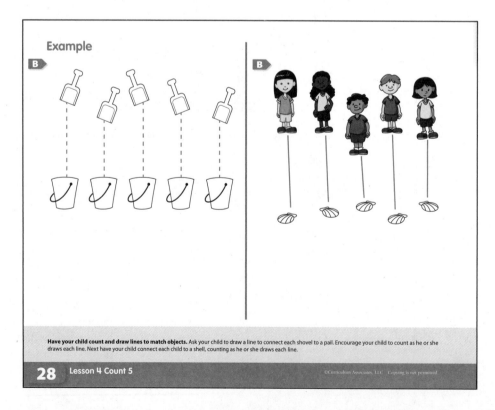

Example

B

B

Have your child count and draw lines to match objects. Ask your child to draw a line to connect each shovel to a pail. Encourage your child to count as he or she draws each line. Next have your child connect each child to a shell, counting as he or she draws each line.

28 Lesson 4 Count 5   ©Curriculum Associates, LLC   Copying is not permitted.

You may wish to assign the following pages for practice after completing the first Guided Practice in *Ready Mathematics.*

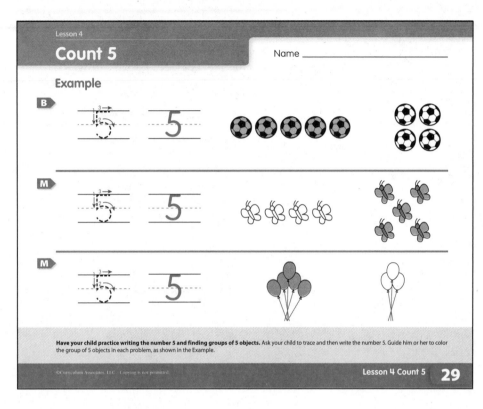

Lesson 4

Count 5

Name _____

Example

B

M

M

Have your child practice writing the number 5 and finding groups of 5 objects. Ask your child to trace and then write the number 5. Guide him or her to color the group of 5 objects in each problem, as shown in the Example.

©Curriculum Associates, LLC   Copying is not permitted.

Lesson 4 Count 5   **29**

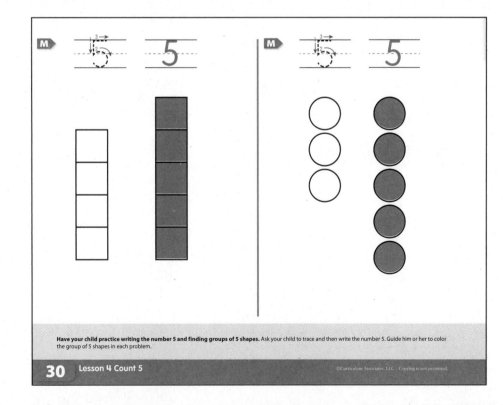

M

M

Have your child practice writing the number 5 and finding groups of 5 shapes. Ask your child to trace and then write the number 5. Guide him or her to color the group of 5 shapes in each problem.

30 Lesson 4 Count 5

©Curriculum Associates, LLC   Copying is not permitted.

Key
B Basic
M Medium
C Challenge

You may wish to assign the following pages for practice after completing the second Guided Practice in *Ready Mathematics*.

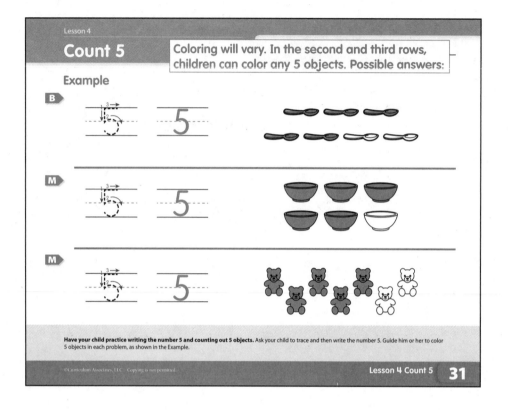

Lesson 4

Count 5

Coloring will vary. In the second and third rows, children can color any 5 objects. Possible answers:

Example

B

M

M

Have your child practice writing the number 5 and counting out 5 objects. Ask your child to trace and then write the number 5. Guide him or her to color 5 objects in each problem, as shown in the Example.

©Curriculum Associates, LLC   Copying is not permitted.

Lesson 4 Count 5   **31**

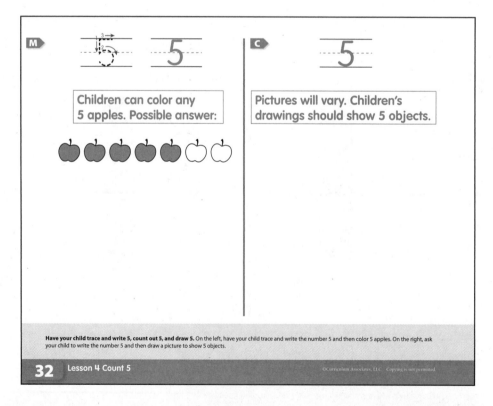

M

Children can color any 5 apples. Possible answer:

C

Pictures will vary. Children's drawings should show 5 objects.

Have your child trace and write 5, count out 5, and draw 5. On the left, have your child trace and write the number 5 and then color 5 apples. On the right, ask your child to write the number 5 and then draw a picture to show 5 objects.

32   Lesson 4 Count 5

©Curriculum Associates, LLC   Copying is not permitted.

You may wish to assign the following pages for practice after completing the
Modeled Instruction in **Ready Mathematics.**

Lesson 5

Compare Within 5

Check that children have colored a group of more than 4 similar objects green, and a group of fewer than 4 similar objects orange.

Have your child find a group of more than 4 similar objects and color those objects green. Then have your child find a group of fewer than 4 similar objects and color those objects orange. Ask your child to color the rest of the picture using different colors.

©Curriculum Associates, LLC   Copying is not permitted

Lesson 5 Compare Within 5   **35**

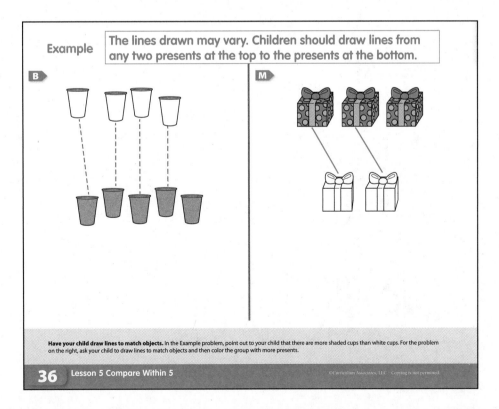

Example

The lines drawn may vary. Children should draw lines from any two presents at the top to the presents at the bottom.

B

M

Have your child draw lines to match objects. In the Example problem, point out to your child that there are more shaded cups than white cups. For the problem on the right, ask your child to draw lines to match objects and then color the group with more presents.

36   Lesson 5 Compare Within 5   ©Curriculum Associates, LLC   Copying is not permitted.

You may wish to assign the following pages for practice after completing the first Guided Practice in *Ready Mathematics.*

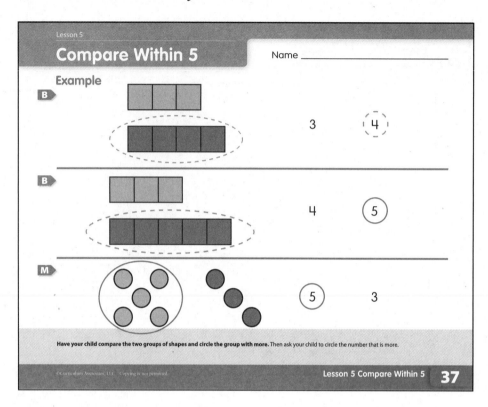

Lesson 5

Compare Within 5   Name _____

Example

B   3   (4)

B   4   (5)

M   (5)   3

Have your child compare the two groups of shapes and circle the group with more. Then ask your child to circle the number that is more.

©Curriculum Associates, LLC   Copying is not permitted.   Lesson 5 Compare Within 5   **37**

Key
B Basic
M Medium
C Challenge

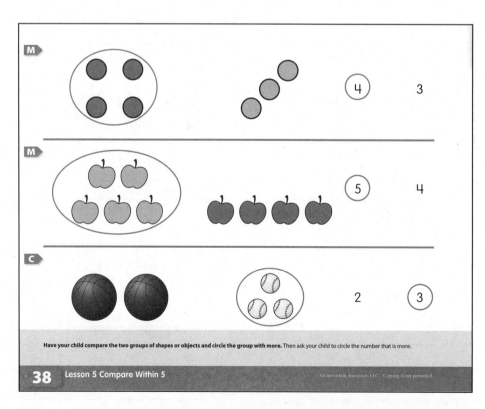

M   (4)   3

M   (5)   4

C   2   (3)

Have your child compare the two groups of shapes or objects and circle the group with more. Then ask your child to circle the number that is more.

38   Lesson 5 Compare Within 5   ©Curriculum Associates, LLC   Copying is not permitted.

You may wish to assign the following pages for practice after completing the second Guided Practice in *Ready Mathematics*.

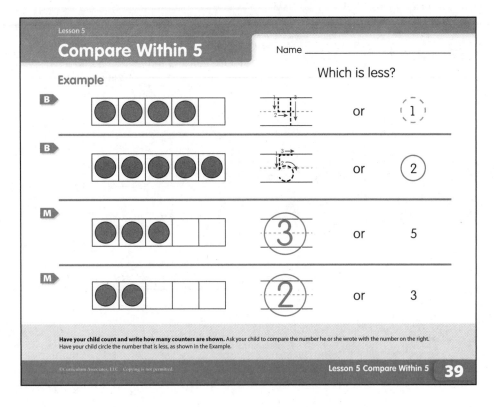

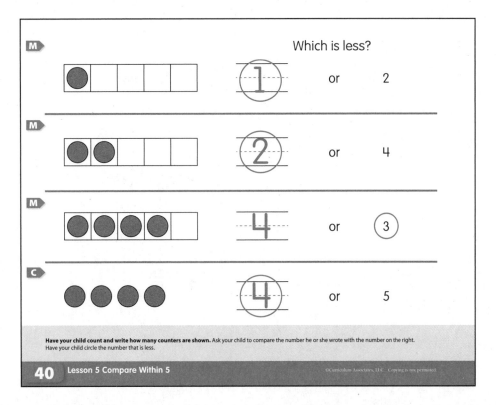

You may wish to assign the following pages for practice after completing the Modeled Instruction in **Ready Mathematics.**

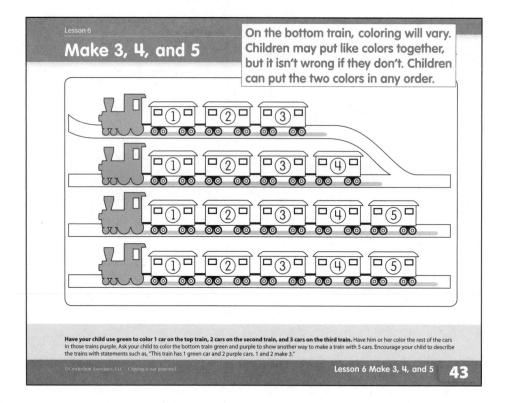

Lesson 6

Make 3, 4, and 5

On the bottom train, coloring will vary. Children may put like colors together, but it isn't wrong if they don't. Children can put the two colors in any order.

Have your child use green to color 1 car on the top train, 2 cars on the second train, and 3 cars on the third train. Have him or her color the rest of the cars in those trains purple. Ask your child to color the bottom train green and purple to show another way to make a train with 5 cars. Encourage your child to describe the trains with statements such as, "This train has 1 green car and 2 purple cars. 1 and 2 make 3."

©Curriculum Associates, LLC   Copying is not permitted.

Lesson 6 Make 3, 4, and 5   **43**

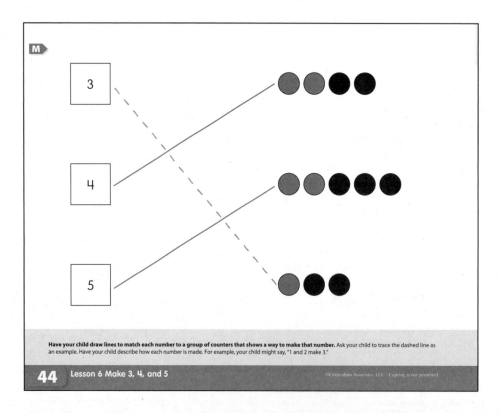

M

3

4

5

Have your child draw lines to match each number to a group of counters that shows a way to make that number. Ask your child to trace the dashed line as an example. Have your child describe how each number is made. For example, your child might say, "1 and 2 make 3."

44   Lesson 6 Make 3, 4, and 5

©Curriculum Associates, LLC   Copying is not permitted.

You may wish to assign the following pages for practice after completing the first Guided Practice in *Ready Mathematics*.

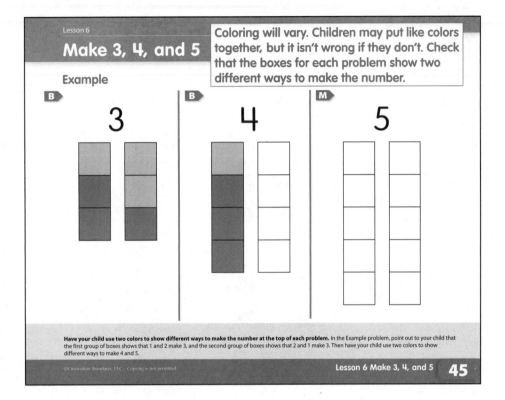

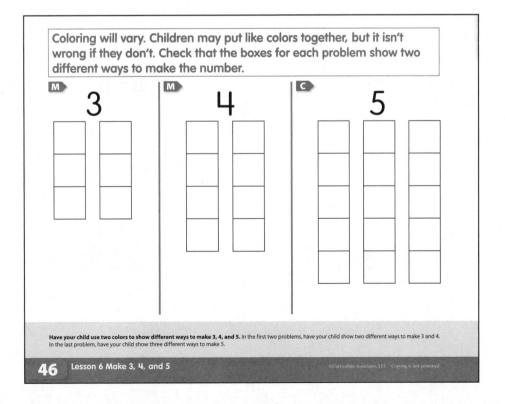

Key

B Basic

M Medium

C Challenge

You may wish to assign the following pages for practice after completing the second Guided Practice in *Ready Mathematics*.

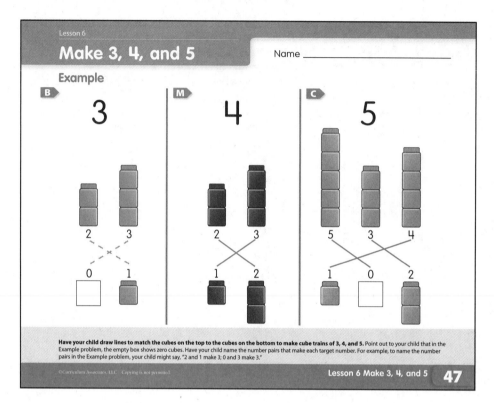

Lesson 6

Make 3, 4, and 5

Name _____

Example

B   3   M   4   C   5

Have your child draw lines to match the cubes on the top to the cubes on the bottom to make cube trains of 3, 4, and 5. Point out to your child that in the Example problem, the empty box shows zero cubes. Have your child name the number pairs that make each target number. For example, to name the number pairs in the Example problem, your child might say, "2 and 1 make 3; 0 and 3 make 3."

©Curriculum Associates, LLC Copying is not permitted.   Lesson 6 Make 3, 4, and 5   **47**

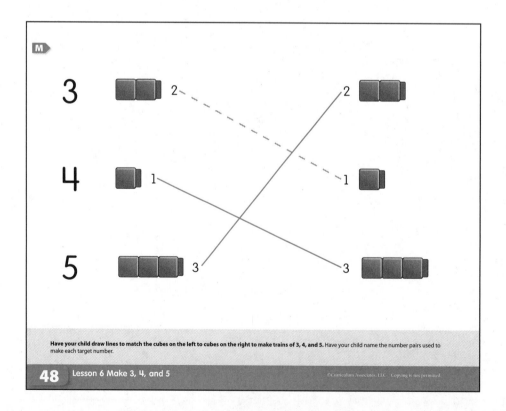

M

3

4

5

Have your child draw lines to match the cubes on the left to cubes on the right to make trains of 3, 4, and 5. Have your child name the number pairs used to make each target number.

48   Lesson 6 Make 3, 4, and 5   ©Curriculum Associates, LLC Copying is not permitted.

Unit 1 Practice

Numbers 1 to 5

Name _____

M   Color 4 △ blue.

Color 5 △ green.

Color 5 △ red.

How many △ are white? _5_

The triangles children color will vary. Check that children color 4 blue, 5 green, and 5 red.

Explain to children that this is a problem that can be solved in different ways. Have children color 4 triangles blue, 5 triangles green, and 5 triangles red. Then count how many triangles are white and write the number.

©Curriculum Associates, LLC   Copying is not permitted.

Unit 1 Practice   **49**

Key

B Basic

M Medium

C Challenge

M ▸ [ ] [ ] [ ] [ ]   [?] _____

_____ [?] in all?   [?] _____

M ▸ [ ] [ ] [ ] [ ] [ ]   [?] _____

_____ [?] in all?   [?] _____

The number of blue and red cubes children color will vary. Check that children's numbers match the drawings and that the totals equal 4 and 5.

Explain to children that this is a problem that can be solved in different ways. Have children color some cubes red and some blue. Then write the number of cubes that are red. Write the number that are blue. Write how many cubes in all.

50   Unit 1 Practice   ©Curriculum Associates, LLC   Copying is not permitted.

Unit 1 Game

Roll and Count

Name _____

1 _____	2 _____

3 _____	4 _____

5 _____

Materials For each child: number cube 1–5, 15 counters or small objects (dried beans, counting bears, etc.), Roll and Count Game Board
How to Play Roll the number cube. Find the box with that number. Write the number, then put that number of objects on the box. Skip a turn if a box is already full. The first player to fill all the boxes wins.

©Curriculum Associates, LLC   Copying is not permitted.   Unit 1 Game   **51**

STEP BY STEP

CCSS Focus - K.CC.A.3, K.CC.B.4 *Embedded SMPs -* 4, 6, 7 **Objective:** Count up to 5 objects. Write numerals 1 through 5.	**Materials:** For each child: number cube (1–5), 15 small classroom objects (dried beans, counting bears, etc.), game board

- **Roll the number cube. Find the box with that number. Write the number, then put that number of objects on the box.** Read the first three sentences of the *How to Play* aloud. After each step, ask children to explain in their own words what to do.

- **Skip a turn if the box for the number you roll is already full. The first player to fill all the boxes wins.** Finish reading *How to Play*, making sure children understand the rules and how to complete the game.

- Roll the number cube, then write that number in the corresponding box on the game board. Model the number by counting out that number of objects and placing them on the box on the board.

- Discuss with children how the number of objects you counted out and the number you wrote are related.

- As children play, observe their 1-to-1 counting skills and provide support as necessary.

Vary the Game For each child, provide 15 connecting cubes of one color and 15 connecting cubes of a different color in place of classroom objects. Give children a copy of the Color the Cubes Recording Sheet (Teacher Resource 2). Have children model numbers 1–5 with cubes, using cubes of two colors to make numbers 2–5. Have them show 4 and 5 two different ways. Then have children color the recording sheet to show all the pairs they used to make the numbers 2–5. Have children discuss the differences in their numbers after play is complete.

ELL Support Use gestures as appropriate and refer to an example round when reviewing the rules.

You may wish to assign the following pages for practice after completing the Modeled Instruction in **Ready Mathematics.**

Lesson 7

Count 6 and 7

Check that children have colored a group of 6 similar objects blue and any 7 windows yellow.

Have your child color a group of 6 similar objects blue. Then have your child choose any 7 windows on the buildings to color yellow. Finally, ask your child to color the rest of the picture using different colors.

©Curriculum Associates, LLC   Copying is not permitted.   Lesson 7 Count 6 and 7   **55**

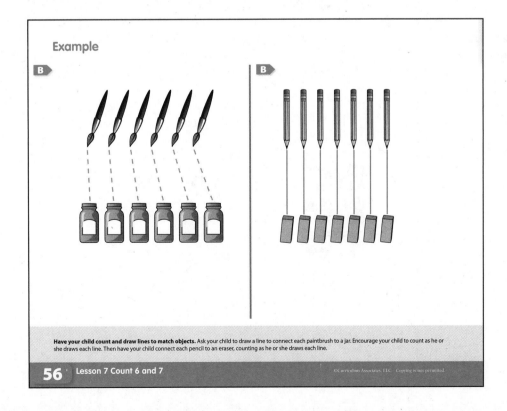

Example

B

B

Have your child count and draw lines to match objects. Ask your child to draw a line to connect each paintbrush to a jar. Encourage your child to count as he or she draws each line. Then have your child connect each pencil to an eraser, counting as he or she draws each line.

56   Lesson 7 Count 6 and 7   ©Curriculum Associates, LLC   Copying is not permitted.

You may wish to assign the following pages for practice after completing the first Guided Practice in *Ready Mathematics*.

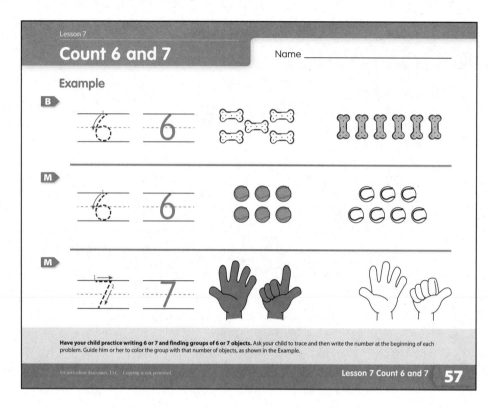

Lesson 7

Count 6 and 7

Name _____

Example

B

M

M

Have your child practice writing 6 or 7 and finding groups of 6 or 7 objects. Ask your child to trace and then write the number at the beginning of each problem. Guide him or her to color the group with that number of objects, as shown in the Example.

©Curriculum Associates, LLC   Copying is not permitted.   Lesson 7 Count 6 and 7   **57**

Key

B Basic

M Medium

C Challenge

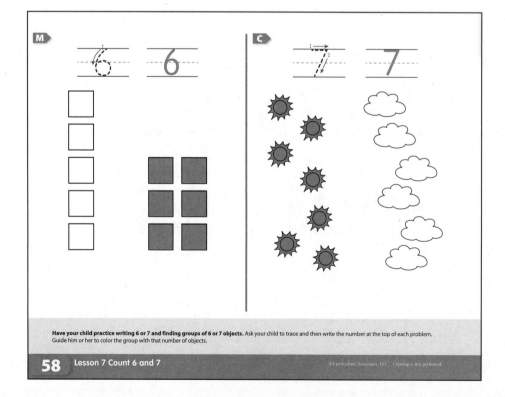

M   **C**

Have your child practice writing 6 or 7 and finding groups of 6 or 7 objects. Ask your child to trace and then write the number at the top of each problem. Guide him or her to color the group with that number of objects.

58   Lesson 7 Count 6 and 7   ©Curriculum Associates, LLC   Copying is not permitted.

You may wish to assign the following pages for practice after completing the second Guided Practice in *Ready Mathematics.*

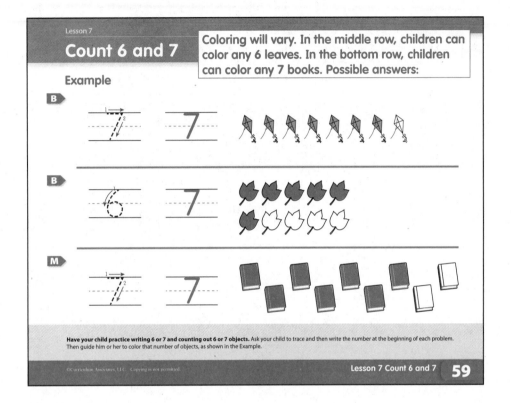

Lesson 7

Count 6 and 7

Coloring will vary. In the middle row, children can color any 6 leaves. In the bottom row, children can color any 7 books. Possible answers:

Example

B

B

M

Have your child practice writing 6 or 7 and counting out 6 or 7 objects. Ask your child to trace and then write the number at the beginning of each problem. Then guide him or her to color that number of objects, as shown in the Example.

©Curriculum Associates, LLC   Copying is not permitted.

Lesson 7 Count 6 and 7   **59**

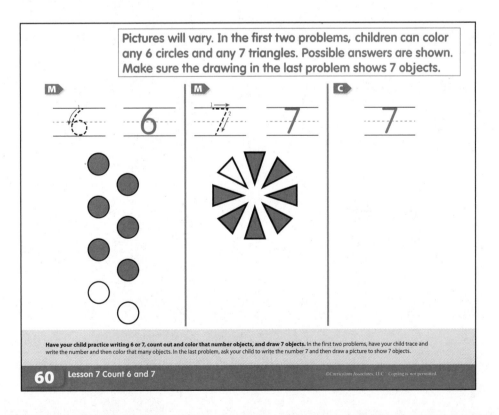

Pictures will vary. In the first two problems, children can color any 6 circles and any 7 triangles. Possible answers are shown. Make sure the drawing in the last problem shows 7 objects.

M

M

C

Have your child practice writing 6 or 7, count out and color that number objects, and draw 7 objects. In the first two problems, have your child trace and write the number and then color that many objects. In the last problem, ask your child to write the number 7 and then draw a picture to show 7 objects.

60   Lesson 7 Count 6 and 7

©Curriculum Associates, LLC   Copying is not permitted.

You may wish to assign the following pages for practice after completing the Modeled Instruction in **Ready Mathematics.**

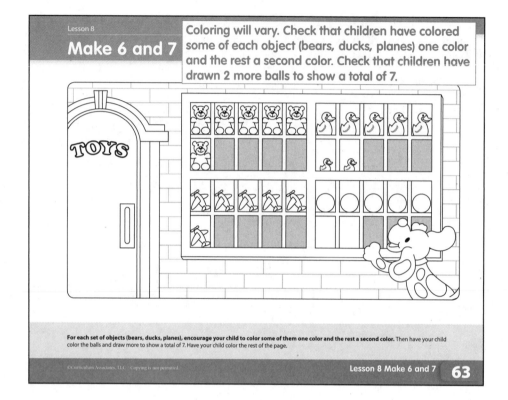

Lesson 8

Make 6 and 7

Coloring will vary. Check that children have colored some of each object (bears, ducks, planes) one color and the rest a second color. Check that children have drawn 2 more balls to show a total of 7.

For each set of objects (bears, ducks, planes), encourage your child to color some of them one color and the rest a second color. Then have your child color the balls and draw more to show a total of 7. Have your child color the rest of the page.

©Curriculum Associates, LLC   Copying is not permitted.   Lesson 8 Make 6 and 7   **63**

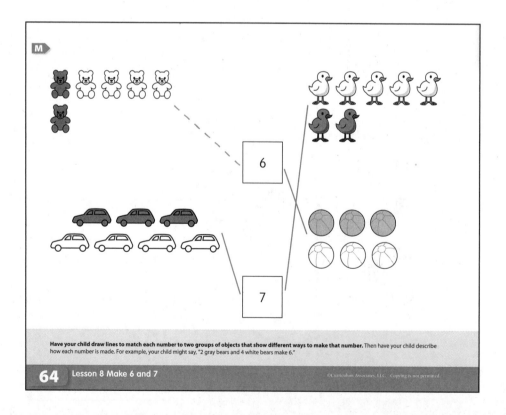

Have your child draw lines to match each number to two groups of objects that show different ways to make that number. Then have your child describe how each number is made. For example, your child might say, "2 gray bears and 4 white bears make 6."

64   Lesson 8 Make 6 and 7   ©Curriculum Associates, LLC   Copying is not permitted.

You may wish to assign the following pages for practice after completing the first Guided Practice in **Ready Mathematics**.

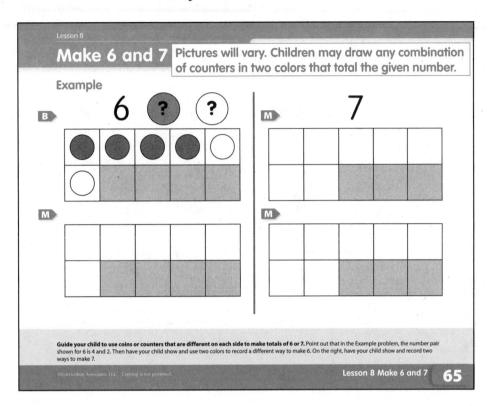

Lesson 8

Make 6 and 7 Pictures will vary. Children may draw any combination of counters in two colors that total the given number.

Example

Guide your child to use coins or counters that are different on each side to make totals of 6 or 7. Point out that in the Example problem, the number pair shown for 6 is 4 and 2. Then have your child show and use two colors to record a different way to make 6. On the right, have your child show and record two ways to make 7.

©Curriculum Associates, LLC Copying is not permitted.   Lesson 8 Make 6 and 7 **65**

Key

B Basic

M Medium

C Challenge

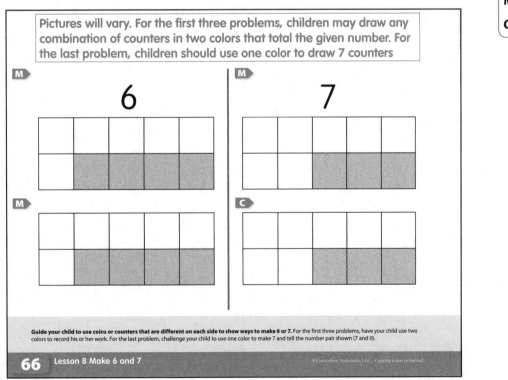

Pictures will vary. For the first three problems, children may draw any combination of counters in two colors that total the given number. For the last problem, children should use one color to draw 7 counters

6

7

Guide your child to use coins or counters that are different on each side to show ways to make 6 or 7. For the first three problems, have your child use two colors to record his or her work. For the last problem, challenge your child to use one color to make 7 and tell the number pair shown (7 and 0).

66 Lesson 8 Make 6 and 7   ©Curriculum Associates, LLC Copying is not permitted.

You may wish to assign the following pages for practice after completing the second Guided Practice in **Ready Mathematics**.

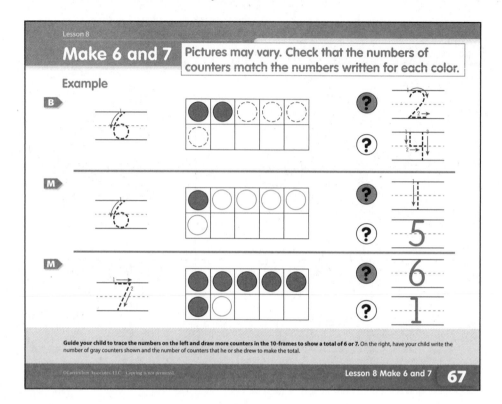

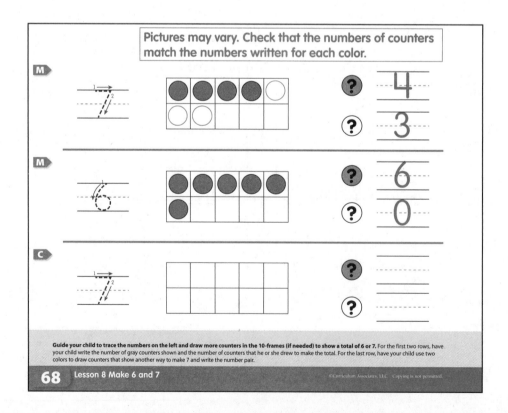

You may wish to assign the following pages for practice after completing the Modeled Instruction in *Ready Mathematics*.

Lesson 9
Count 8 and 9

Coloring will vary. Check that children have colored a group of 8 similar objects one color, and a group of 9 similar objects another color.

Have your child color a group of 8 similar objects. Then have your child use a different color to color a group of 9 similar objects. Have your child color the rest of the picture.

©Curriculum Associates, LLC   Copying is not permitted.   Lesson 9 Count 8 and 9   **71**

B ▶

Have your child count and draw lines to match objects. Have your child draw a line to connect each umbrella to a child. Encourage your child to count as he or she draws each line and tell the total number of lines drawn. Then have your child connect each child to a rain hat, counting as he or she draws each line.

72   Lesson 9 Count 8 and 9   ©Curriculum Associates, LLC   Copying is not permitted.

You may wish to assign the following pages for practice after completing the first Guided Practice in *Ready Mathematics.*

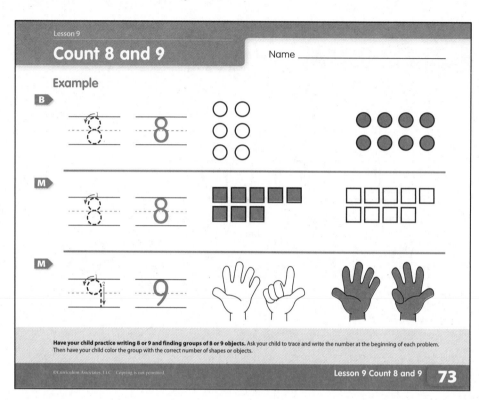

Lesson 9

Count 8 and 9

Name _____

Example

B ▶

M ▶

M ▶

Have your child practice writing 8 or 9 and finding groups of 8 or 9 objects. Ask your child to trace and write the number at the beginning of each problem. Then have your child color the group with the correct number of shapes or objects.

©Curriculum Associates, LLC   Copying is not permitted.   Lesson 9 Count 8 and 9 **73**

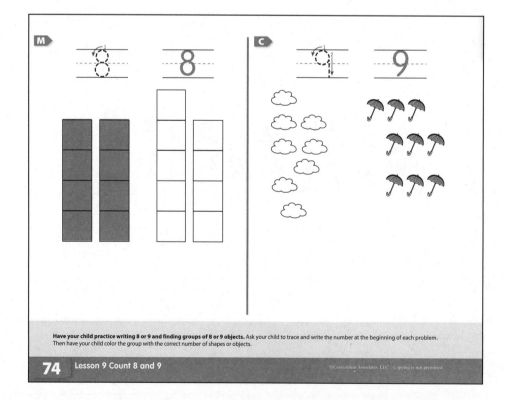

M

C

Have your child practice writing 8 or 9 and finding groups of 8 or 9 objects. Ask your child to trace and write the number at the beginning of each problem. Then have your child color the group with the correct number of shapes or objects.

74 Lesson 9 Count 8 and 9   ©Curriculum Associates, LLC   Copying is not permitted.

You may wish to assign the following pages for practice after completing the second Guided Practice in **Ready Mathematics**.

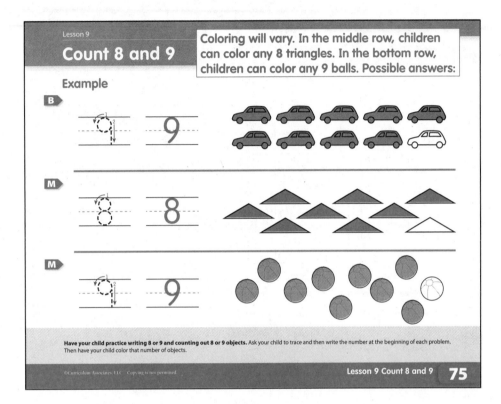

Lesson 9

Count 8 and 9

Coloring will vary. In the middle row, children can color any 8 triangles. In the bottom row, children can color any 9 balls. Possible answers:

Example

B 9

M 8

M 9

Have your child practice writing 8 or 9 and counting out 8 or 9 objects. Ask your child to trace and then write the number at the beginning of each problem. Then have your child color that number of objects.

©Curriculum Associates, LLC   Copying is not permitted.

Lesson 9 Count 8 and 9   **75**

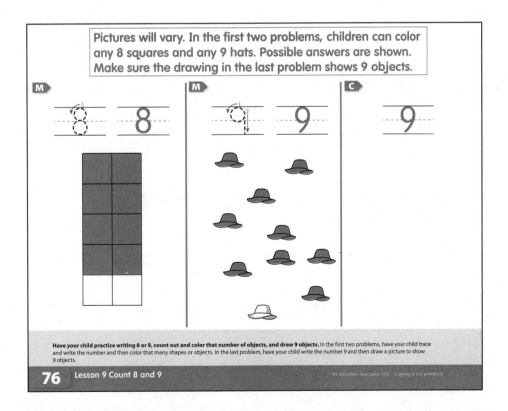

Pictures will vary. In the first two problems, children can color any 8 squares and any 9 hats. Possible answers are shown. Make sure the drawing in the last problem shows 9 objects.

M 8

M 9

C 9

Have your child practice writing 8 or 9, count out and color that number of objects, and draw 9 objects. In the first two problems, have your child trace and write the number and then color that many shapes or objects. In the last problem, have your child write the number 9 and then draw a picture to show 9 objects.

76   Lesson 9 Count 8 and 9

©Curriculum Associates, LLC   Copying is not permitted.

You may wish to assign the following pages for practice after completing the Modeled Instruction in **Ready Mathematics.**

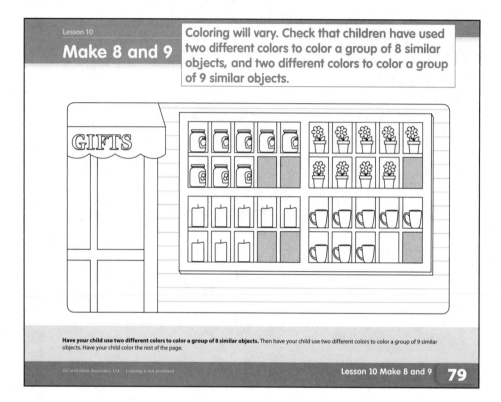

Lesson 10

Make 8 and 9

Coloring will vary. Check that children have used two different colors to color a group of 8 similar objects, and two different colors to color a group of 9 similar objects.

GIFTS

Have your child use two different colors to color a group of 8 similar objects. Then have your child use two different colors to color a group of 9 similar objects. Have your child color the rest of the page.

©Curriculum Associates, LLC Copying is not permitted.   Lesson 10 Make 8 and 9   **79**

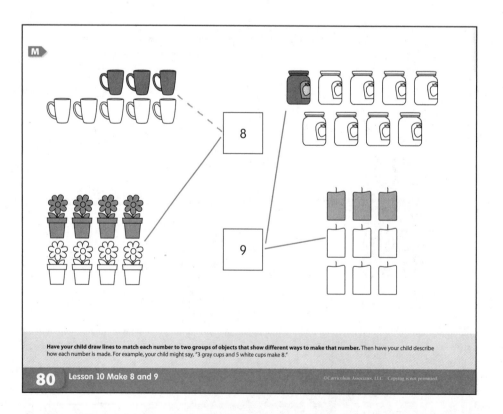

M

8

9

Have your child draw lines to match each number to two groups of objects that show different ways to make that number. Then have your child describe how each number is made. For example, your child might say, "3 gray cups and 5 white cups make 8."

80 Lesson 10 Make 8 and 9   ©Curriculum Associates, LLC   Copying is not permitted.

You may wish to assign the following pages for practice after completing the first Guided Practice in *Ready Mathematics*.

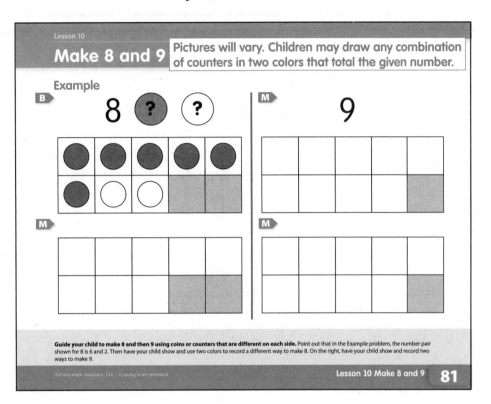

Lesson 10

Make 8 and 9

Pictures will vary. Children may draw any combination of counters in two colors that total the given number.

Example

B ▸ 8 ? ?

M ▸ 9

M ▸

M ▸

Guide your child to make 8 and then 9 using coins or counters that are different on each side. Point out that in the Example problem, the number pair shown for 8 is 6 and 2. Then have your child show and use two colors to record a different way to make 8. On the right, have your child show and record two ways to make 9.

©Curriculum Associates, LLC   Copying is not permitted.

Lesson 10 Make 8 and 9   **81**

Key

B Basic

M Medium

C Challenge

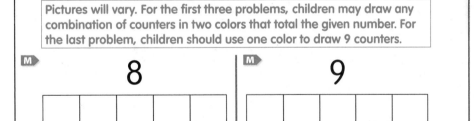

Pictures will vary. For the first three problems, children may draw any combination of counters in two colors that total the given number. For the last problem, children should use one color to draw 9 counters.

M ▸ 8

M ▸ 9

M ▸

C ▸

Guide your child to make 8 and then 9 using coins or counters that are different on each side. For the first three problems, have your child use two colors to record his or her work. For the last problem, challenge your child to use one color to make 9 and tell the number pair shown (9 and 0).

82   Lesson 10 Make 8 and 9

©Curriculum Associates, LLC.   Copying is not permitted.

You may wish to assign the following pages for practice after completing the second Guided Practice in *Ready Mathematics*.

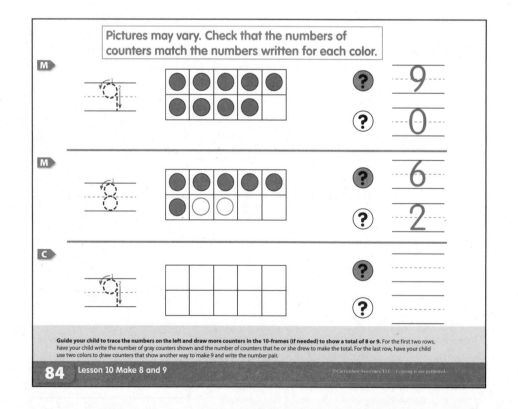

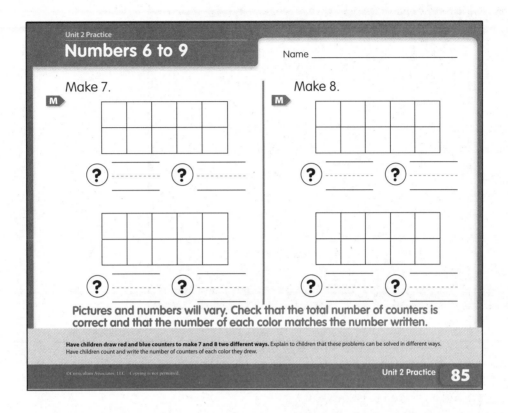

Unit 2 Practice
Numbers 6 to 9

Name _____

Make 7.

Ⓜ

❓ _____ ❓ _____

❓ _____ ❓ _____

Make 8.

Ⓜ

❓ _____ ❓ _____

❓ _____ ❓ _____

Pictures and numbers will vary. Check that the total number of counters is correct and that the number of each color matches the number written.

Have children draw red and blue counters to make 7 and 8 two different ways. Explain to children that these problems can be solved in different ways. Have children count and write the number of counters of each color they drew.

©Curriculum Associates, LLC Copying is not permitted.   **Unit 2 Practice** **85**

Key

B Basic

M Medium

C Challenge

Ⓒ

How many dogs? ___9___

Draw 1 🦴 for each dog.

Children may use circles to show each bone. Check that children draw 9 bones.

Have children count and write the number of dogs, then draw one bone for each dog pictured. Allow children to find their own strategies for determining how many bones to draw.

86 Unit 2 Practice   ©Curriculum Associates, LLC Copying is not permitted.

Unit 2 Game
Match 6, 7, 8, and 9

Name _____

Materials For each pair: 1 set of Dot Cards; for each child: Match 6, 7, 8, and 9 Game Board
How to Play Take a dot card. Tell how many dots are on the card. Find the 10-frame with that many dots. Write the number to label that 10-frame. Skip a turn if the 10-frame is already used. The first player to label all the 10-frames wins.

©Curriculum Associates, LLC   Copying is not permitted.   Unit 2 Game   **87**

STEP BY STEP

| **CCSS Focus** - K.CC.A.3, K.CC.B.4a, K.CC.B.4b, K.CC.B.5, K.OA.A.3   *Embedded SMPs* - 1, 2, 3, 7

 Objective: Count 6, 7, 8, and 9. Develop familiarity with number pairs for 6, 7, 8, and 9. Match domino and 10-frame representations of 6, 7, 8, and 9. | **Materials:** For each pair: Dot Cards 1–9 (Teacher Resource 4); for each child: game board |

- **Take a dot card. Tell how many dots are on the card. Find the 10-frame with that many. Write the number to label that 10-frame.** Read the first four sentences of the *How to Play* aloud. After each step, ask children to explain in their own words what to do.

- **Skip a turn if the 10-frame is already used. The first player to label all the 10-frames wins.** Finish reading *How to Play*, making sure children understand the rules and how to complete the game.

- Make a stack of dot cards and model taking a card. Think aloud as you count all the dots. For example, say: *I see 2 dots and 5 dots. 1, 2, 3, 4, 5, 6, 7. There are 7 dots altogether.*

- Then model deciding which 10-frame shows 7, and writing 7 below it. Think aloud first to demonstrate why the 10-frame with 6 is incorrect.

- Encourage children to explain to their partner why the dominoes and 10-frames match. Observe as children play to provide support and to look for the strategies they use.

Vary the Game To simplify the game, use only dot cards that show numbers as a combination of 5 dots and some more. This makes the relationship to the 10-frame more apparent.

ELL Support For children who count fluently in another language, this game can be played initially with no English. This allows them to fully engage with the math while they work on learning English number words.

You may wish to assign the following pages for practice after completing the Modeled Instruction in *Ready Mathematics.*

Lesson 11

Count 10

Check that children have colored groups of 10 objects.

Have your child use different colors to color groups of 10. Then have your child color the rest of the picture.

©Curriculum Associates, LLC   Copying is not permitted.

Lesson 11 Count 10   **91**

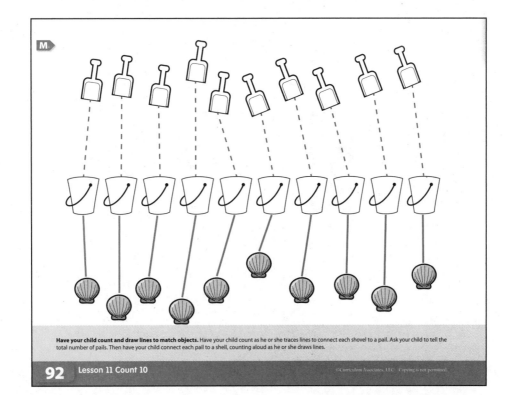

Have your child count and draw lines to match objects. Have your child count as he or she traces lines to connect each shovel to a pail. Ask your child to tell the total number of pails. Then have your child connect each pail to a shell, counting aloud as he or she draws lines.

92   Lesson 11 Count 10   ©Curriculum Associates, LLC   Copying is not permitted.

You may wish to assign the following pages for practice after completing the first Guided Practice in **Ready Mathematics**.

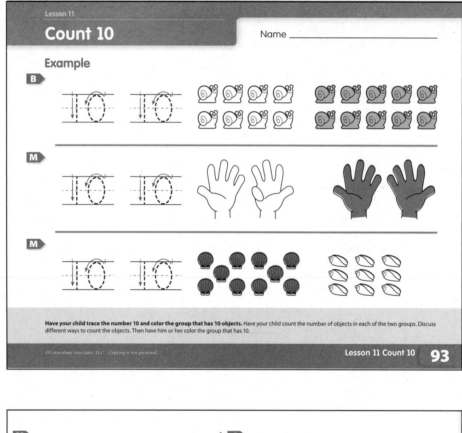

Lesson 11

Count 10

Name _____

Example

B

M

M

Have your child trace the number 10 and color the group that has 10 objects. Have your child count the number of objects in each of the two groups. Discuss different ways to count the objects. Then have him or her color the group that has 10.

©Curriculum Associates, LLC Copying is not permitted.

Lesson 11 Count 10 **93**

Key

B Basic

M Medium

C Challenge

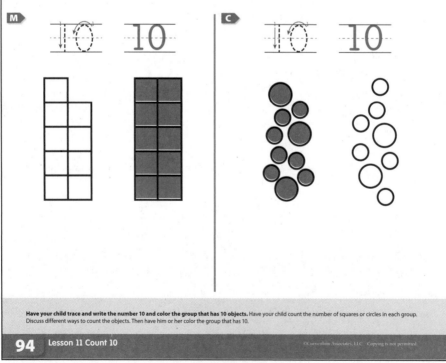

M

C

Have your child trace and write the number 10 and color the group that has 10 objects. Have your child count the number of squares or circles in each group. Discuss different ways to count the objects. Then have him or her color the group that has 10.

94 Lesson 11 Count 10

©Curriculum Associates, LLC Copying is not permitted.

You may wish to assign the following pages for practice after completing the second Guided Practice in *Ready Mathematics.*

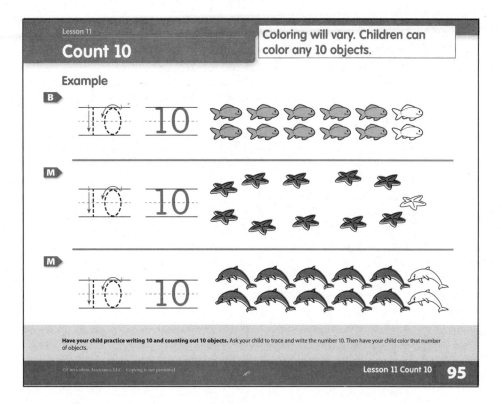

Lesson 11

Count 10

Coloring will vary. Children can color any 10 objects.

Example

Have your child practice writing 10 and counting out 10 objects. Ask your child to trace and write the number 10. Then have your child color that number of objects.

©Curriculum Associates, LLC Copying is not permitted.   Lesson 11 Count 10 **95**

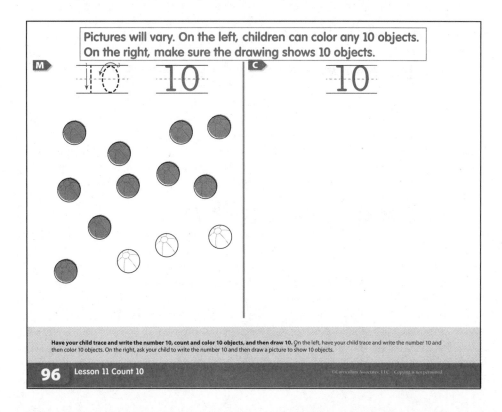

Pictures will vary. On the left, children can color any 10 objects. On the right, make sure the drawing shows 10 objects.

Have your child trace and write the number 10, count and color 10 objects, and then draw 10. On the left, have your child trace and write the number 10 and then color 10 objects. On the right, ask your child to write the number 10 and then draw a picture to show 10 objects.

96 Lesson 11 Count 10   ©Curriculum Associates, LLC Copying is not permitted.

You may wish to assign the following pages for practice after completing the Modeled Instruction in *Ready Mathematics.*

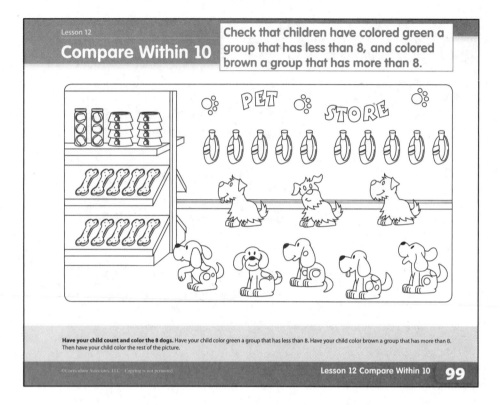

Lesson 12

Compare Within 10

Check that children have colored green a group that has less than 8, and colored brown a group that has more than 8.

Have your child count and color the 8 dogs. Have your child color green a group that has less than 8. Have your child color brown a group that has more than 8. Then have your child color the rest of the picture.

©Curriculum Associates, LLC Copying is not permitted.

Lesson 12 Compare Within 10   **99**

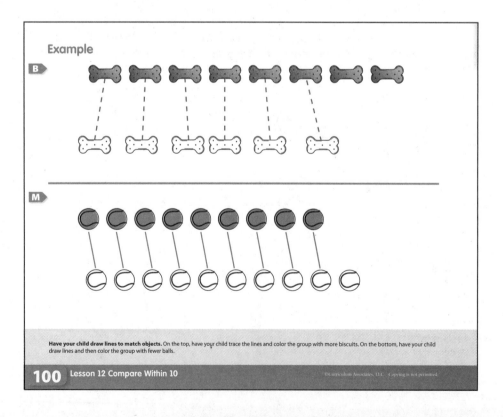

Example

B

M

Have your child draw lines to match objects. On the top, have your child trace the lines and color the group with more biscuits. On the bottom, have your child draw lines and then color the group with fewer balls.

100 Lesson 12 Compare Within 10   ©Curriculum Associates, LLC Copying is not permitted.

You may wish to assign the following pages for practice after completing the
first Guided Practice in *Ready Mathematics.*

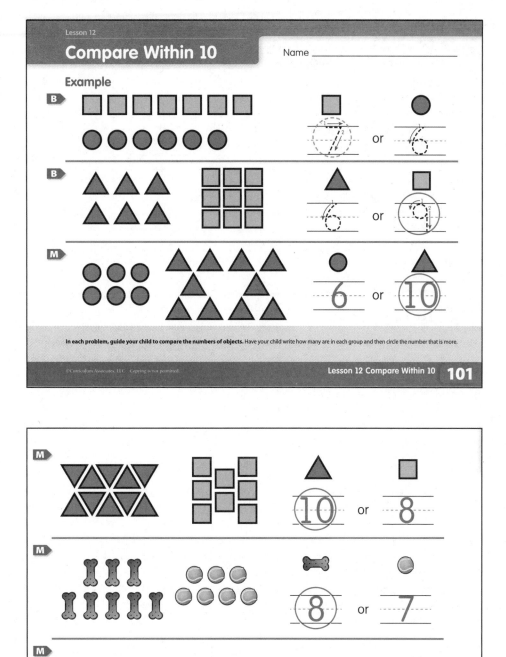

Lesson 12 Compare Within 10 **101**

Key

B Basic
M Medium
C Challenge

102 Lesson 12 Compare Within 10

You may wish to assign the following pages for practice after completing the second Guided Practice in **Ready Mathematics.**

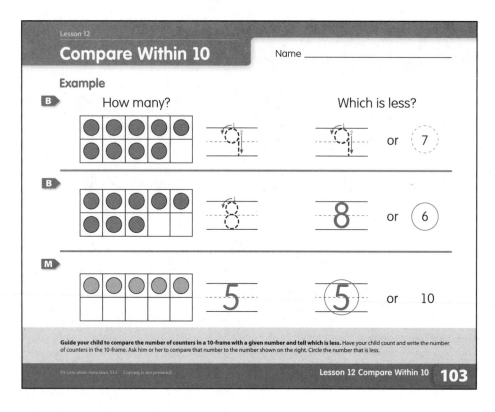

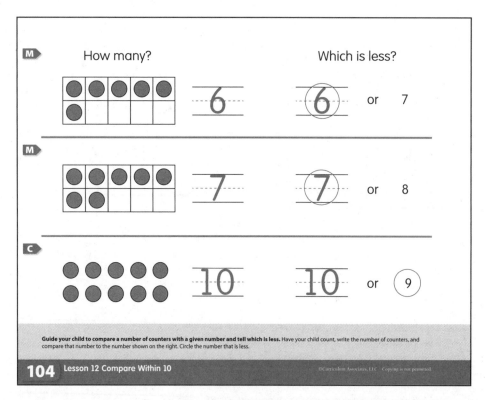

You may wish to assign the following pages for practice after completing the Modeled Instruction in *Ready Mathematics*.

Lesson 13

Make 10

Check that children have colored two groups of 10, using two colors for each group to show different number pairs.

Have your child use two colors to color a group of 10. Then have your child use two colors to color another group of 10, this time showing a different number pair. Have your child color the rest of the page.

©Curriculum Associates, LLC   Copying is not permitted.

Lesson 13 Make 10   **107**

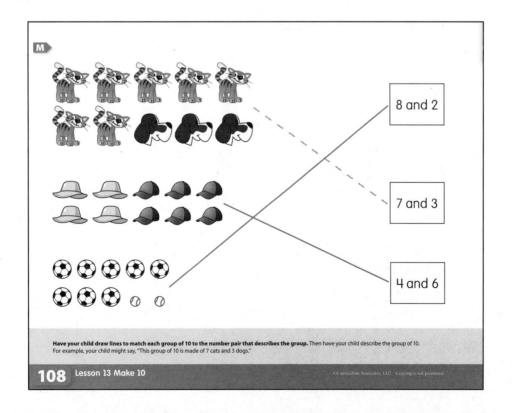

Have your child draw lines to match each group of 10 to the number pair that describes the group. Then have your child describe the group of 10. For example, your child might say, "This group of 10 is made of 7 cats and 3 dogs."

108 Lesson 13 Make 10

©Curriculum Associates, LLC   Copying is not permitted.

You may wish to assign the following pages for practice after completing the
first Guided Practice in **Ready Mathematics.**

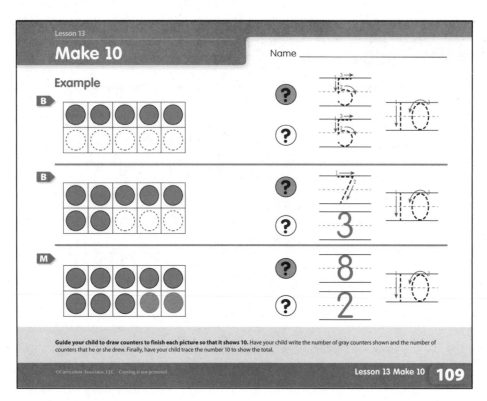

Lesson 13
Make 10   Name _____

Example

Guide your child to draw counters to finish each picture so that it shows 10. Have your child write the number of gray counters shown and the number of counters that he or she drew. Finally, have your child trace the number 10 to show the total.

©Curriculum Associates, LLC   Copying is not permitted.   Lesson 13 Make 10 **109**

Key

B Basic
M Medium
C Challenge

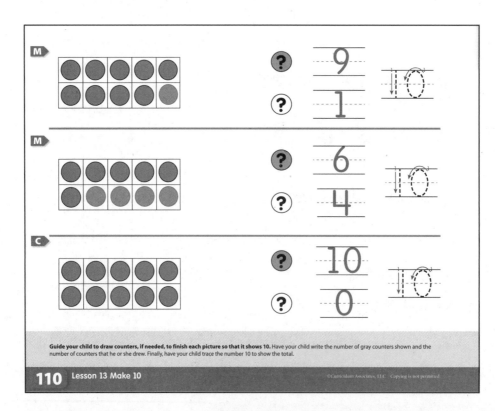

Guide your child to draw counters, if needed, to finish each picture so that it shows 10. Have your child write the number of gray counters shown and the number of counters that he or she drew. Finally, have your child trace the number 10 to show the total.

110 Lesson 13 Make 10   ©Curriculum Associates, LLC   Copying is not permitted.

You may wish to assign the following pages for practice after completing the second Guided Practice in *Ready Mathematics*.

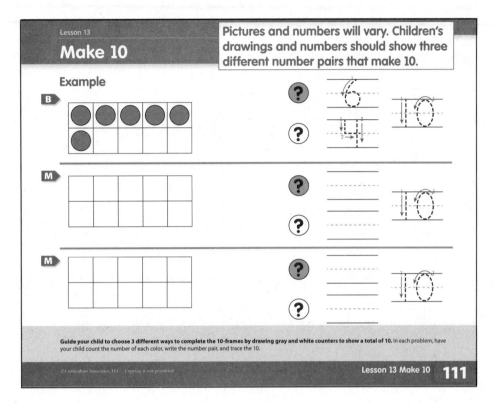

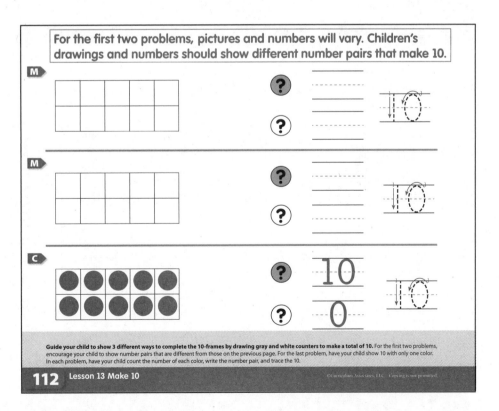

Unit 3 Practice
Numbers to 10

Name _____

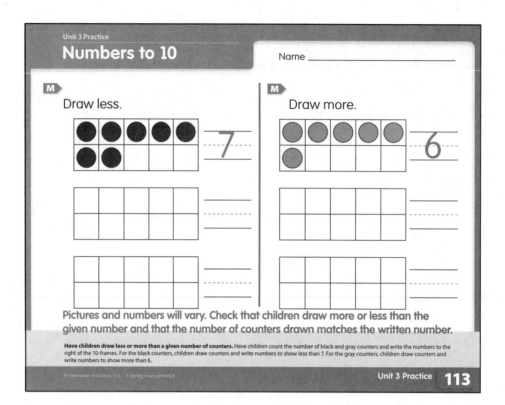

M Draw less.

7

M Draw more.

6

Pictures and numbers will vary. Check that children draw more or less than the given number and that the number of counters drawn matches the written number.

Have children draw less or more than a given number of counters. Have children count the number of black and gray counters and write the numbers to the right of the 10-frames. For the black counters, children draw counters and write numbers to show less than 7. For the gray counters, children draw counters and write numbers to show more than 6.

Unit 3 Practice **113**

Key
B Basic
M Medium
C Challenge

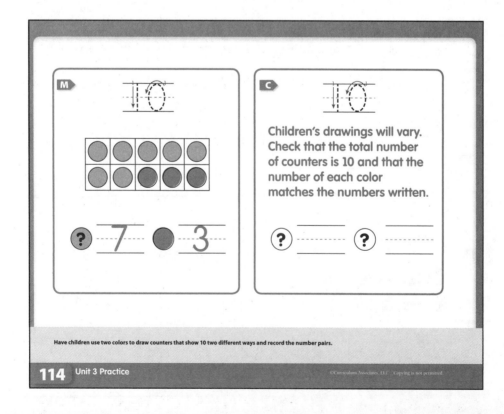

M

10

? — 7   🔵 — 3

C

10

Children's drawings will vary. Check that the total number of counters is 10 and that the number of each color matches the numbers written.

? _____   ? _____

Have children use two colors to draw counters that show 10 two different ways and record the number pairs.

114 Unit 3 Practice

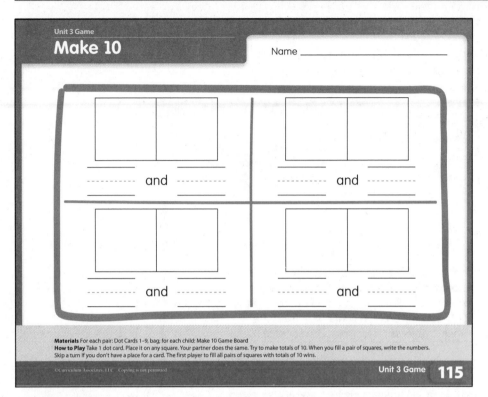

Unit 3 Game

Make 10

Name _____

and

and

and

and

Materials For each pair: Dot Cards 1–9, bag; for each child: Make 10 Game Board
How to Play Take 1 dot card. Place it on any square. Your partner does the same. Try to make totals of 10. When you fill a pair of squares, write the numbers.
Skip a turn if you don't have a place for a card. The first player to fill all pairs of squares with totals of 10 wins.

©Curriculum Associates, LLC   Copying is not permitted   Unit 3 Game **115**

STEP BY STEP

CCSS Focus - K.CC.A.3, K.CC.B.4a, K.CC.B.4b, K.CC.B.5, K.CC.C.6, K.OA.A.3, K.OA.A.4 *Embedded SMPs* - 1, 2, 7 **Objective:** Use dot cards to find number pairs for 10. Practice 1-to-1 counting to 10.	**Materials:** For each pair: Dot Cards 1–9 (Teacher Resource 6) bag; for each child: game board

- **Take 1 dot card. Place it on any square. Your partner does the same. Try to make totals of 10. When you fill a pair of squares, write the numbers.** Read the first five sentences of the *How to Play* aloud. After each step, ask children to explain in their own words what to do.

- **Skip a turn if you don't have a place for a card. The first player to fill all the pairs of squares with totals of 10 wins.** Finish reading *How to Play*, making sure children understand the rules and how to complete the game.

- Model taking a 5 dot card and placing it on the game board. Then show a 6 dot card and discuss why this card cannot go on the square next to the 5. Place the 6 on a different square.

- Pull a 4 card and place it next to the 6. Model writing 4 and 6 on the game board.

- Have children put their cards in the bag to start the game. Tell children to place the card back in the bag if they cannot play.

- Observe as children play the game. Point out errors and encourage children to correct them. Watch for strategies they use to make 10.

Vary the Game When children fill a pair of squares, have them compare the two numbers, telling which is "more," "less," or "fewer."

Challenge Use Number Cards 1–9 (Teacher Resource 7) instead of dot cards. Place pairs of number cards that total 10 to fill all the squares.

You may wish to assign the following pages for practice after completing the Modeled Instruction in **Ready Mathematics.**

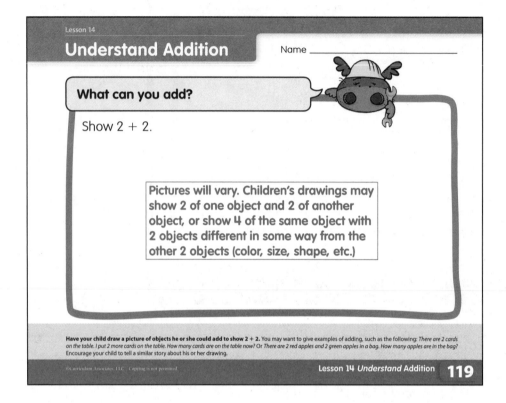

Lesson 14

Understand Addition

Name _____

What can you add?

Show 2 + 2.

> Pictures will vary. Children's drawings may show 2 of one object and 2 of another object, or show 4 of the same object with 2 objects different in some way from the other 2 objects (color, size, shape, etc.)

Have your child draw a picture of objects he or she could add to show 2 + 2. You may want to give examples of adding, such as the following: *There are 2 cards on the table. I put 2 more cards on the table. How many cards are on the table now?* Or *There are 2 red apples and 2 green apples in a bag. How many apples are in the bag?* Encourage your child to tell a similar story about his or her drawing.

©Curriculum Associates, LLC Copying is not permitted.   **Lesson 14** *Understand* Addition **119**

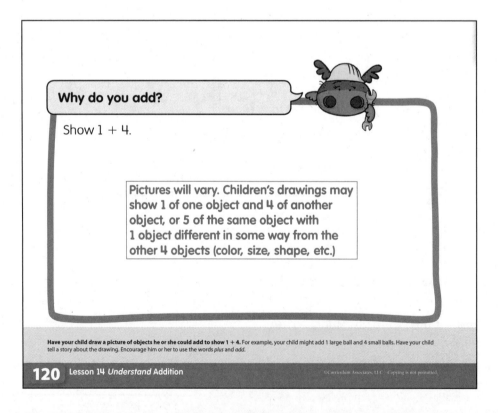

Why do you add?

Show 1 + 4.

> Pictures will vary. Children's drawings may show 1 of one object and 4 of another object, or 5 of the same object with 1 object different in some way from the other 4 objects (color, size, shape, etc.)

Have your child draw a picture of objects he or she could add to show 1 + 4. For example, your child might add 1 large ball and 4 small balls. Have your child tell a story about the drawing. Encourage him or her to use the words *plus* and *add*.

120 **Lesson 14** *Understand* Addition   ©Curriculum Associates, LLC Copying is not permitted.

You may wish to assign the following pages for practice after completing the Guided Exploration in *Ready Mathematics.*

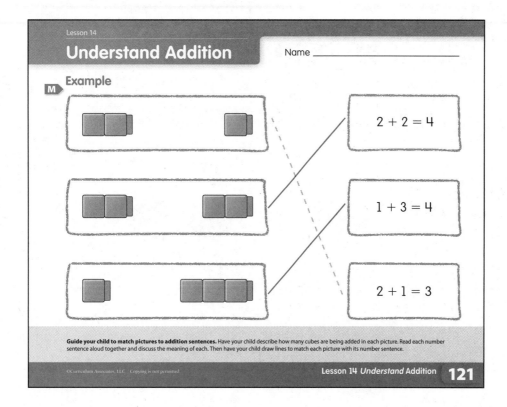

Lesson 14

Understand Addition

Name _____

M ▶ **Example**

Guide your child to match pictures to addition sentences. Have your child describe how many cubes are being added in each picture. Read each number sentence aloud together and discuss the meaning of each. Then have your child draw lines to match each picture with its number sentence.

©Curriculum Associates, LLC   Copying is not permitted.

Lesson 14 *Understand* Addition   **121**

Key

B Basic

M Medium

C Challenge

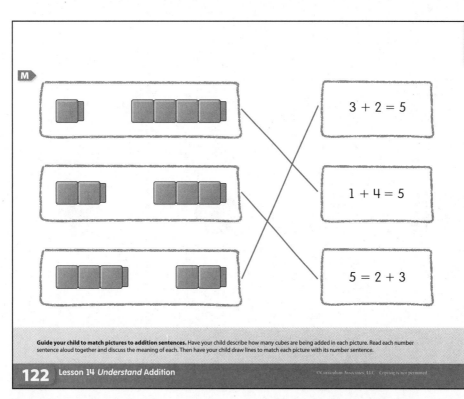

M ▶

Guide your child to match pictures to addition sentences. Have your child describe how many cubes are being added in each picture. Read each number sentence aloud together and discuss the meaning of each. Then have your child draw lines to match each picture with its number sentence.

122 **Lesson 14** *Understand* Addition

©Curriculum Associates, LLC   Copying is not permitted.

You may wish to assign the following pages for practice after completing the Guided Practice in **Ready Mathematics.**

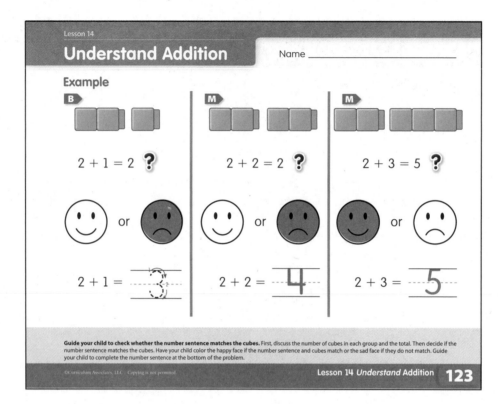

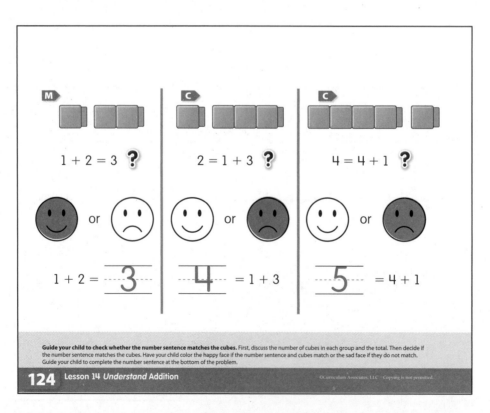

You may wish to assign the following pages for practice after completing the Modeled Instruction in *Ready Mathematics.*

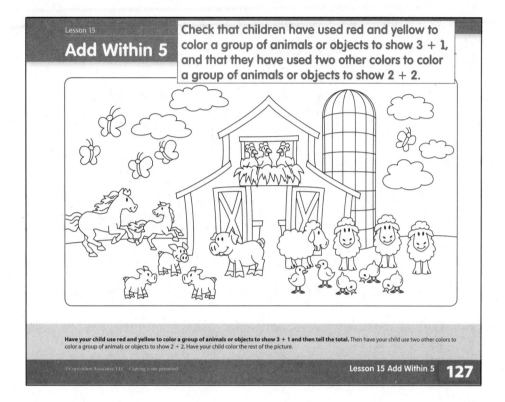

Lesson 15

Add Within 5

Check that children have used red and yellow to color a group of animals or objects to show 3 + 1, and that they have used two other colors to color a group of animals or objects to show 2 + 2.

Have your child use red and yellow to color a group of animals or objects to show 3 + 1 and then tell the total. Then have your child use two other colors to color a group of animals or objects to show 2 + 2. Have your child color the rest of the picture.

©Curriculum Associates, LLC   Copying is not permitted.   **Lesson 15 Add Within 5** **127**

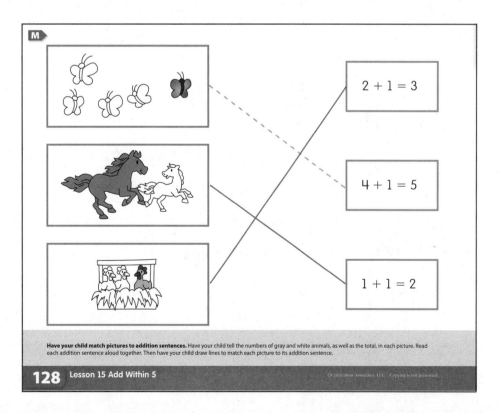

M

$2 + 1 = 3$

$4 + 1 = 5$

$1 + 1 = 2$

Have your child match pictures to addition sentences. Have your child tell the numbers of gray and white animals, as well as the total, in each picture. Read each addition sentence aloud together. Then have your child draw lines to match each picture to its addition sentence.

128 **Lesson 15 Add Within 5**   ©Curriculum Associates, LLC   Copying is not permitted.

You may wish to assign the following pages for practice after completing the first Guided Practice in *Ready Mathematics.*

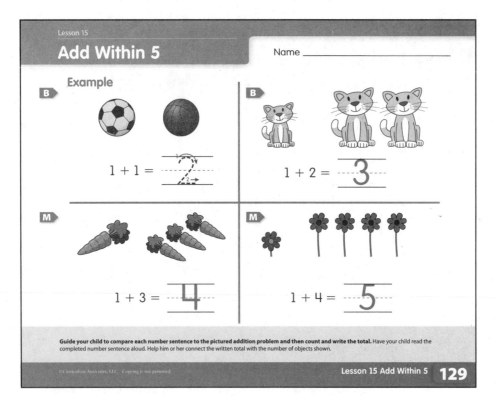

Lesson 15

Add Within 5

Name _____

B Example

$1 + 1 = 2$

B

$1 + 2 = 3$

M

$1 + 3 = 4$

M

$1 + 4 = 5$

Guide your child to compare each number sentence to the pictured addition problem and then count and write the total. Have your child read the completed number sentence aloud. Help him or her connect the written total with the number of objects shown.

©Curriculum Associates, LLC   Copying is not permitted.

Lesson 15 Add Within 5   **129**

Key

B Basic

M Medium

C Challenge

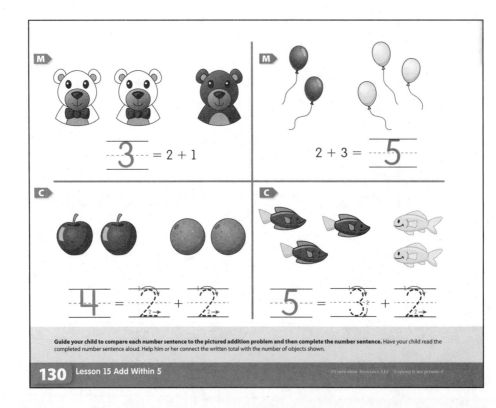

M

$3 = 2 + 1$

M

$2 + 3 = 5$

C

$4 = 2 + 2$

C

$5 = 3 + 2$

Guide your child to compare each number sentence to the pictured addition problem and then complete the number sentence. Have your child read the completed number sentence aloud. Help him or her connect the written total with the number of objects shown.

130   Lesson 15 Add Within 5

©Curriculum Associates, LLC   Copying is not permitted.

You may wish to assign the following pages for practice after completing the second Guided Practice in *Ready Mathematics.*

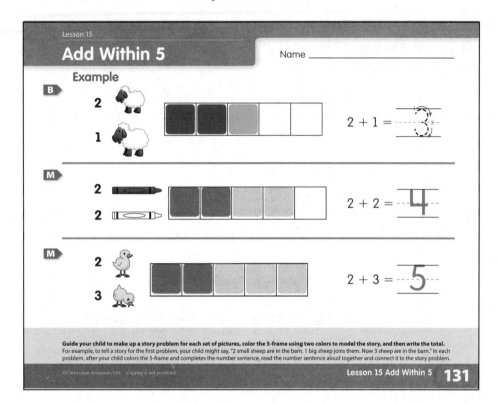

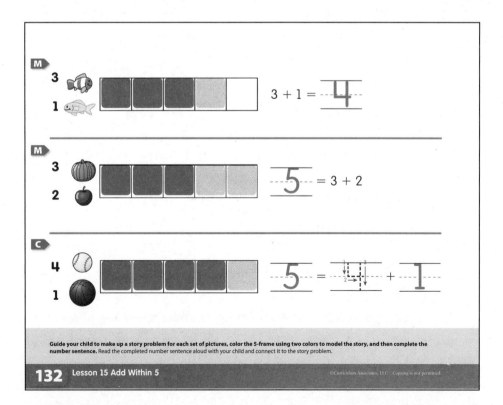

You may wish to assign the following pages for practice after completing the Modeled Instruction in **Ready Mathematics**.

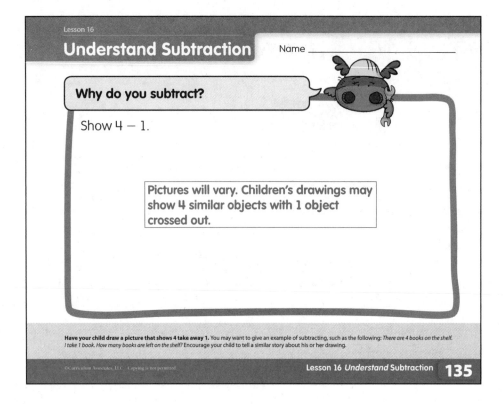

Lesson 16

Understand Subtraction

Name _____

Why do you subtract?

Show 4 − 1.

> Pictures will vary. Children's drawings may show 4 similar objects with 1 object crossed out.

Have your child draw a picture that shows 4 take away 1. You may want to give an example of subtracting, such as the following: *There are 4 books on the shelf. I take 1 book. How many books are left on the shelf?* Encourage your child to tell a similar story about his or her drawing.

©Curriculum Associates, LLC   Copying is not permitted   **Lesson 16** *Understand* Subtraction   **135**

What can you subtract?

Show 3 − 2.

> Pictures will vary. Children's drawings may show 3 similar objects with 2 objects crossed out.

Have your child draw a picture of objects he or she could subtract to show 3 take away 2. For example, your child might draw 3 crackers with 2 crossed out. Have your child tell a story about the drawing using the words *take away, minus,* and *subtract.*

136   **Lesson 16** *Understand* Subtraction   ©Curriculum Associates, LLC   Copying is not permitted

You may wish to assign the following pages for practice after completing the Guided Exploration in *Ready Mathematics*.

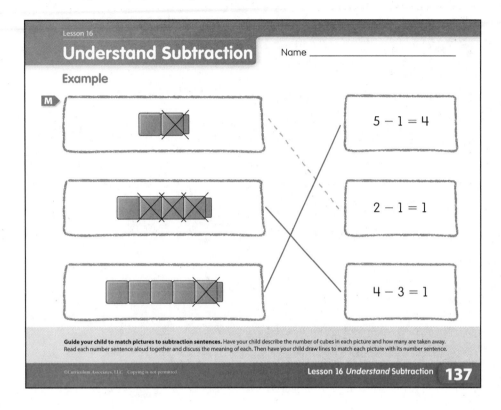

Lesson 16

Understand Subtraction   Name _____

Example

M

5 − 1 = 4

2 − 1 = 1

4 − 3 = 1

Guide your child to match pictures to subtraction sentences. Have your child describe the number of cubes in each picture and how many are taken away. Read each number sentence aloud together and discuss the meaning of each. Then have your child draw lines to match each picture with its number sentence.

Lesson 16 *Understand* Subtraction   **137**

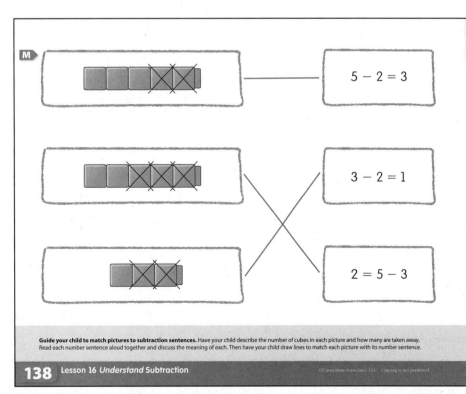

M

5 − 2 = 3

3 − 2 = 1

2 = 5 − 3

Guide your child to match pictures to subtraction sentences. Have your child describe the number of cubes in each picture and how many are taken away. Read each number sentence aloud together and discuss the meaning of each. Then have your child draw lines to match each picture with its number sentence.

138   **Lesson 16** *Understand* Subtraction   ©Curriculum Associates, LLC Copying is not permitted.

You may wish to assign the following pages for practice after completing the Guided Practice in **Ready Mathematics.**

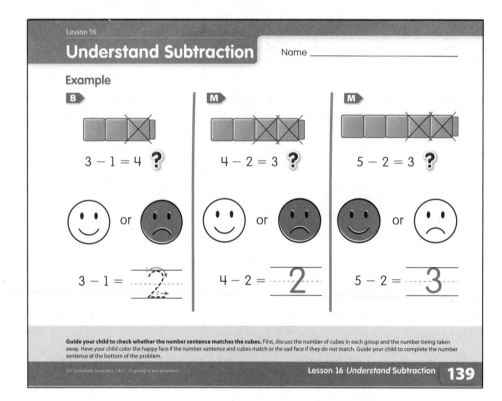

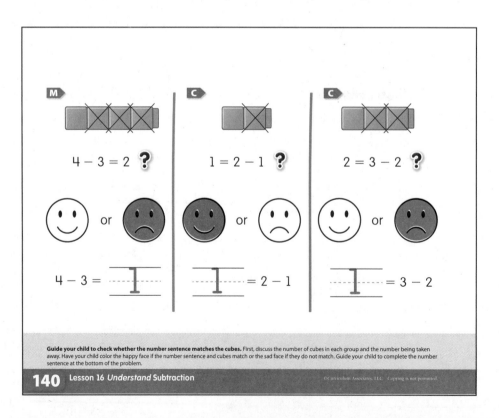

You may wish to assign the following pages for practice after completing the
Modeled Instruction in *Ready Mathematics.*

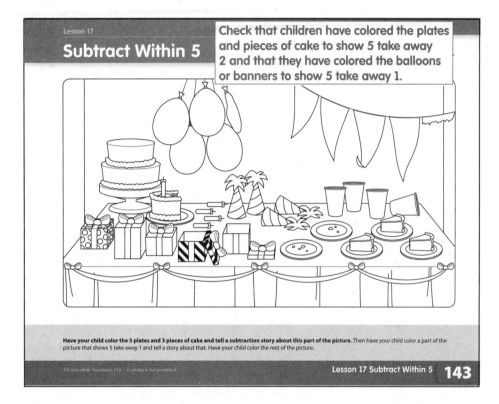

Lesson 17

Subtract Within 5

Check that children have colored the plates
and pieces of cake to show 5 take away
2 and that they have colored the balloons
or banners to show 5 take away 1.

Have your child color the 5 plates and 3 pieces of cake and tell a subtraction story about this part of the picture. Then have your child color a part of the
picture that shows 5 take away 1 and tell a story about that. Have your child color the rest of the picture.

©Curriculum Associates, LLC   Copying is not permitted.   Lesson 17 Subtract Within 5   **143**

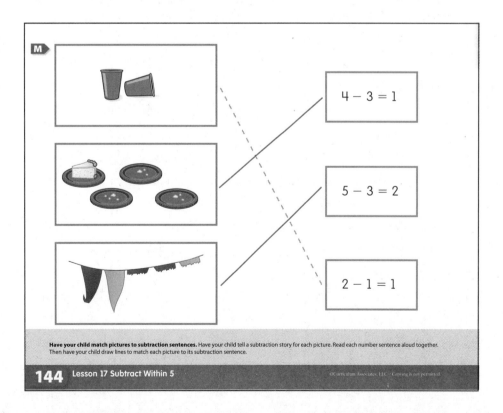

M

$$4 - 3 = 1$$

$$5 - 3 = 2$$

$$2 - 1 = 1$$

Have your child match pictures to subtraction sentences. Have your child tell a subtraction story for each picture. Read each number sentence aloud together.
Then have your child draw lines to match each picture to its subtraction sentence.

144   Lesson 17 Subtract Within 5   ©Curriculum Associates, LLC   Copying is not permitted.

You may wish to assign the following pages for practice after completing the first Guided Practice in *Ready Mathematics.*

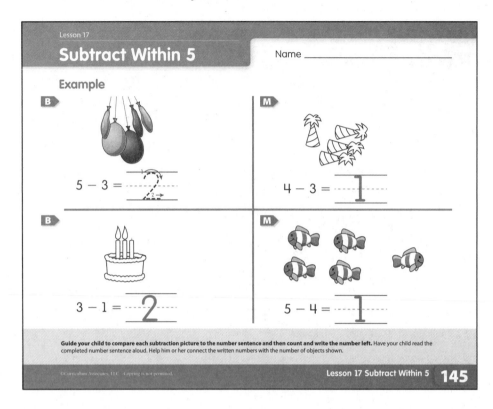

Lesson 17

Subtract Within 5

Name _____

Example

B ▶

$5 - 3 = 2$

M ▶

$4 - 3 = 1$

B ▶

$3 - 1 = 2$

M ▶

$5 - 4 = 1$

Guide your child to compare each subtraction picture to the number sentence and then count and write the number left. Have your child read the completed number sentence aloud. Help him or her connect the written numbers with the number of objects shown.

©Curriculum Associates, LLC   Copying is not permitted.   Lesson 17 Subtract Within 5   **145**

Key

B Basic

M Medium

C Challenge

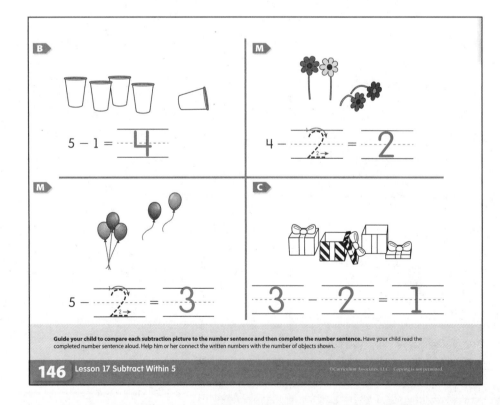

B ▶

$5 - 1 = 4$

M ▶

$4 - 2 = 2$

M ▶

$5 - 2 = 3$

C ▶

$3 - 2 = 1$

Guide your child to compare each subtraction picture to the number sentence and then complete the number sentence. Have your child read the completed number sentence aloud. Help him or her connect the written numbers with the number of objects shown.

146   Lesson 17 Subtract Within 5   ©Curriculum Associates, LLC   Copying is not permitted.

You may wish to assign the following pages for practice after completing the second Guided Practice in **Ready Mathematics**.

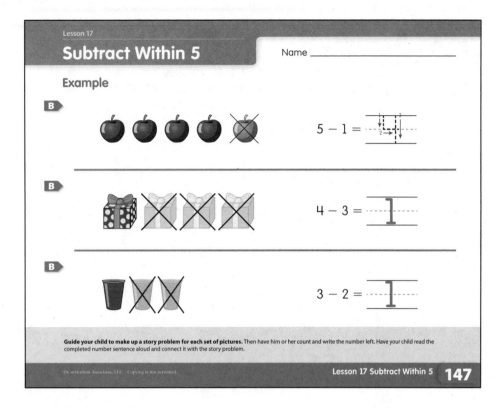

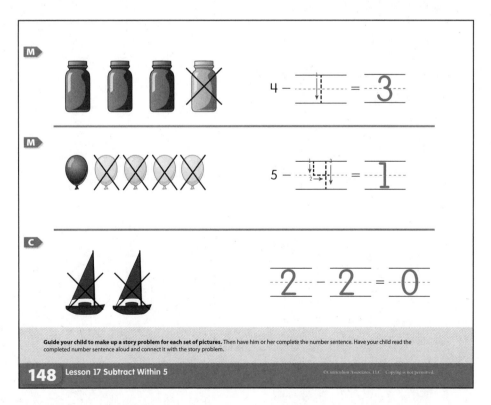

You may wish to assign the following pages for practice after completing the Modeled Instruction in **Ready Mathematics.**

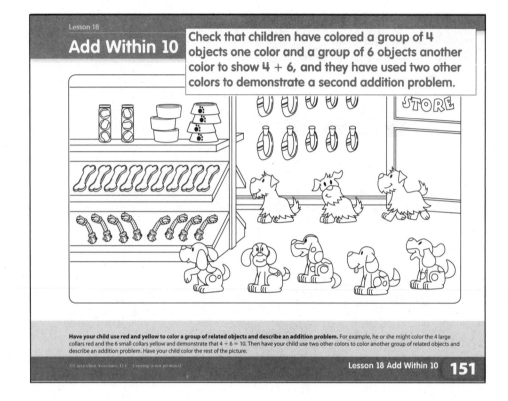

Lesson 18

Add Within 10

Check that children have colored a group of 4 objects one color and a group of 6 objects another color to show 4 + 6, and they have used two other colors to demonstrate a second addition problem.

STORE

Have your child use red and yellow to color a group of related objects and describe an addition problem. For example, he or she might color the 4 large collars red and the 6 small collars yellow and demonstrate that 4 + 6 = 10. Then have your child use two other colors to color another group of related objects and describe an addition problem. Have your child color the rest of the picture.

©Curriculum Associates, LLC   Copying is not permitted.

Lesson 18 Add Within 10   **151**

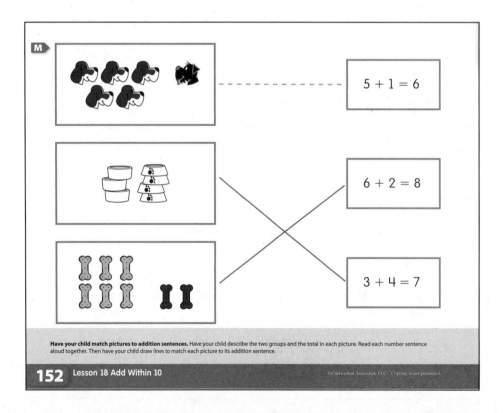

M

$5 + 1 = 6$

$6 + 2 = 8$

$3 + 4 = 7$

Have your child match pictures to addition sentences. Have your child describe the two groups and the total in each picture. Read each number sentence aloud together. Then have your child draw lines to match each picture to its addition sentence.

152   Lesson 18 Add Within 10

©Curriculum Associates, LLC   Copying is not permitted.

You may wish to assign the following pages for practice after completing the first Guided Practice in *Ready Mathematics*.

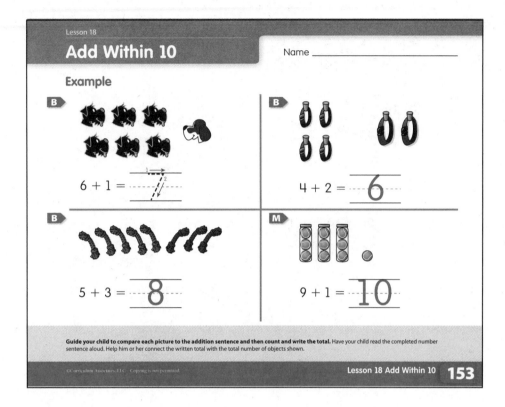

Lesson 18

Add Within 10

Name _____

Example

B 6 + 1 = 7

B 4 + 2 = 6

B 5 + 3 = 8

M 9 + 1 = 10

Guide your child to compare each picture to the addition sentence and then count and write the total. Have your child read the completed number sentence aloud. Help him or her connect the written total with the total number of objects shown.

©Curriculum Associates, LLC   Copying is not permitted.   Lesson 18 Add Within 10 **153**

Key
B Basic
M Medium
C Challenge

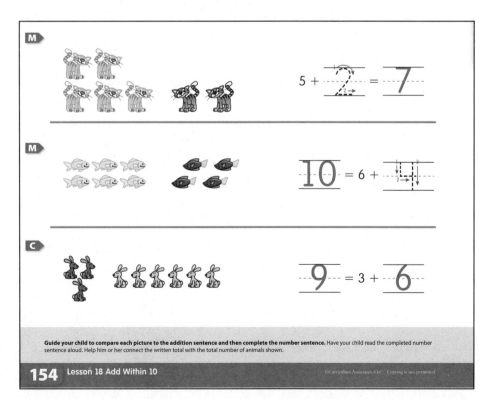

M 5 + 2 = 7

M 10 = 6 + 4

C 9 = 3 + 6

Guide your child to compare each picture to the addition sentence and then complete the number sentence. Have your child read the completed number sentence aloud. Help him or her connect the written total with the total number of animals shown.

154 Lesson 18 Add Within 10   ©Curriculum Associates, LLC   Copying is not permitted.

You may wish to assign the following pages for practice after completing the second Guided Practice in **Ready Mathematics.**

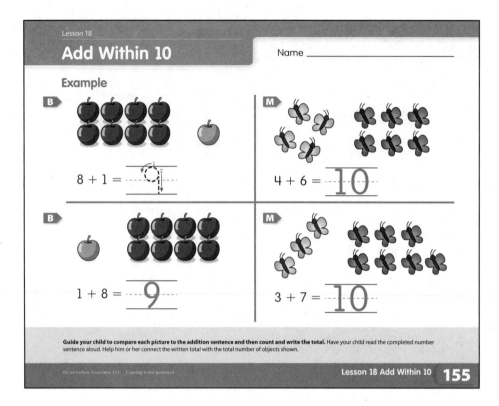

Lesson 18

Add Within 10

Name _____

Example

B
$8 + 1 = 9$

M
$4 + 6 = 10$

B
$1 + 8 = 9$

M
$3 + 7 = 10$

Guide your child to compare each picture to the addition sentence and then count and write the total. Have your child read the completed number sentence aloud. Help him or her connect the written total with the total number of objects shown.

©Curriculum Associates, LLC   Copying is not permitted.

Lesson 18 Add Within 10   **155**

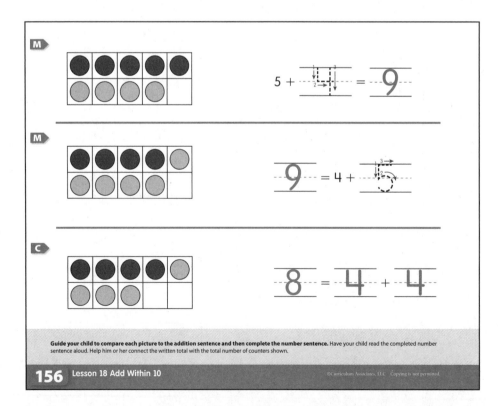

M
$5 + 4 = 9$

M
$9 = 4 + 5$

C
$8 = 4 + 4$

Guide your child to compare each picture to the addition sentence and then complete the number sentence. Have your child read the completed number sentence aloud. Help him or her connect the written total with the total number of counters shown.

156   Lesson 18 Add Within 10

©Curriculum Associates, LLC   Copying is not permitted.

You may wish to assign the following pages for practice after completing the Modeled Instruction in **Ready Mathematics**.

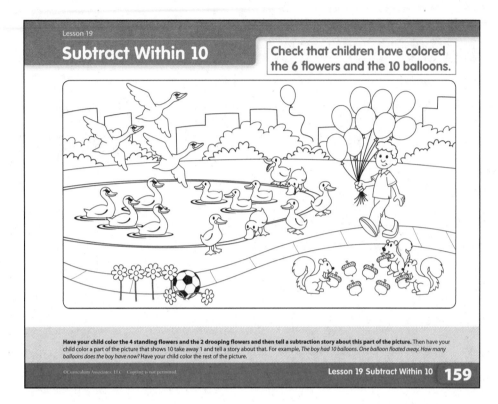

Lesson 19

Subtract Within 10

Check that children have colored the 6 flowers and the 10 balloons.

Have your child color the 4 standing flowers and the 2 drooping flowers and then tell a subtraction story about this part of the picture. Then have your child color a part of the picture that shows 10 take away 1 and tell a story about that. For example, *The boy had 10 balloons. One balloon floated away. How many balloons does the boy have now?* Have your child color the rest of the picture.

©Curriculum Associates, LLC   Copying is not permitted.   Lesson 19 Subtract Within 10   **159**

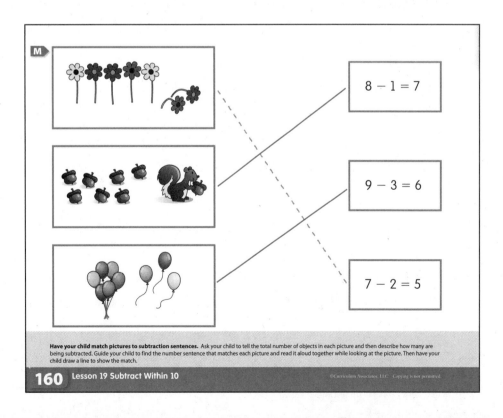

M

$8 - 1 = 7$

$9 - 3 = 6$

$7 - 2 = 5$

Have your child match pictures to subtraction sentences. Ask your child to tell the total number of objects in each picture and then describe how many are being subtracted. Guide your child to find the number sentence that matches each picture and read it aloud together while looking at the picture. Then have your child draw a line to show the match.

160   Lesson 19 Subtract Within 10   ©Curriculum Associates, LLC   Copying is not permitted.

You may wish to assign the following pages for practice after completing the
first Guided Practice in **Ready Mathematics**.

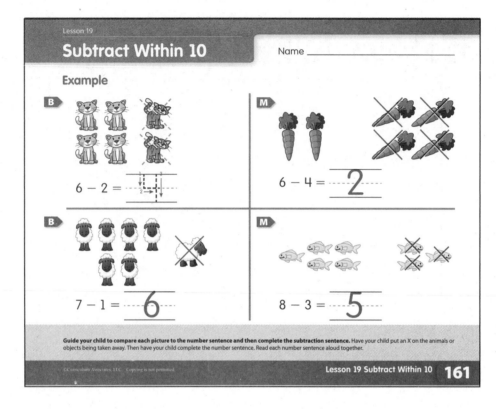

Lesson 19

Subtract Within 10

Name _____

Example

B $6 - 2 = $

M $6 - 4 = \underline{2}$

B $7 - 1 = \underline{6}$

M $8 - 3 = \underline{5}$

Guide your child to compare each picture to the number sentence and then complete the subtraction sentence. Have your child put an X on the animals or objects being taken away. Then have your child complete the number sentence. Read each number sentence aloud together.

©Curriculum Associates, LLC   Copying is not permitted.   Lesson 19 Subtract Within 10   **161**

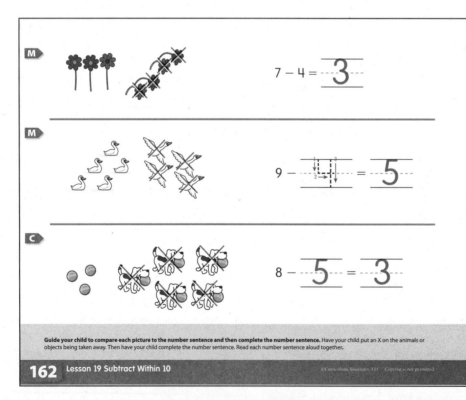

M $7 - 4 = \underline{3}$

M $9 - = \underline{5}$

C $8 - \underline{5} = \underline{3}$

Guide your child to compare each picture to the number sentence and then complete the number sentence. Have your child put an X on the animals or objects being taken away. Then have your child complete the number sentence. Read each number sentence aloud together.

162   Lesson 19 Subtract Within 10   ©Curriculum Associates, LLC   Copying is not permitted.

You may wish to assign the following pages for practice after completing the second Guided Practice in *Ready Mathematics*.

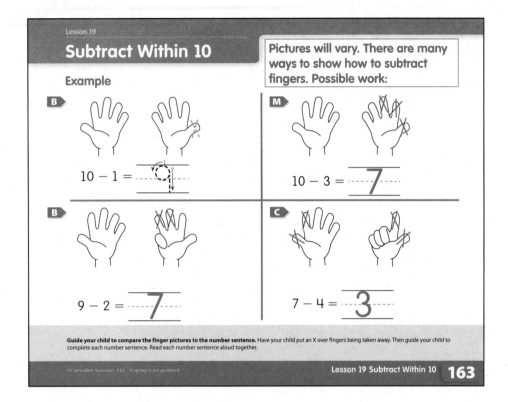

Lesson 19

Subtract Within 10

Pictures will vary. There are many ways to show how to subtract fingers. Possible work:

Example

B $10 - 1 = \underline{}$

M $10 - 3 = \underline{7}$

B $9 - 2 = \underline{7}$

C $7 - 4 = \underline{3}$

Guide your child to compare the finger pictures to the number sentence. Have your child put an X over fingers being taken away. Then guide your child to complete each number sentence. Read each number sentence aloud together.

©Curriculum Associates, LLC   Copying is not permitted.   Lesson 19 Subtract Within 10   **163**

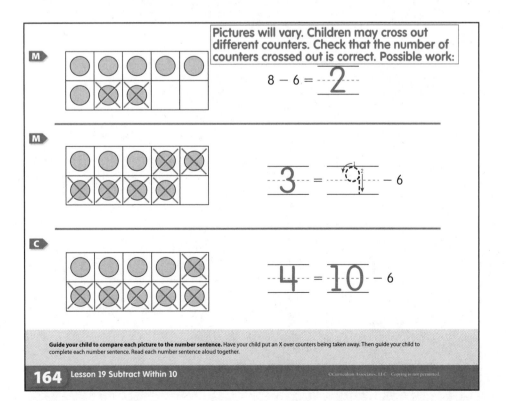

Pictures will vary. Children may cross out different counters. Check that the number of counters crossed out is correct. Possible work:

M $8 - 6 = \underline{2}$

M $\underline{3} = \underline{} - 6$

C $\underline{4} = \underline{10} - 6$

Guide your child to compare each picture to the number sentence. Have your child put an X over counters being taken away. Then guide your child to complete each number sentence. Read each number sentence aloud together.

164 Lesson 19 Subtract Within 10   ©Curriculum Associates, LLC   Copying is not permitted.

You may wish to assign the following pages for practice after completing the Modeled Instruction in *Ready Mathematics.*

Lesson 20

Practice Facts to 5

Check that children have colored the 5 children in the picture.

Have your child color the 5 children in the picture. Then have him or her tell an addition story and a subtraction story about the 5 children. For example, *Two girls and 3 boys are at the beach. How many children are at the beach?* and *There are 5 friends playing. One friend leaves. How many friends are playing now?* As your child colors the rest of the picture, encourage him or her to share an addition story and a subtraction story for each group of objects.

©Curriculum Associates, LLC   Copying is not permitted.   Lesson 20 Practice Facts to 5   **167**

M

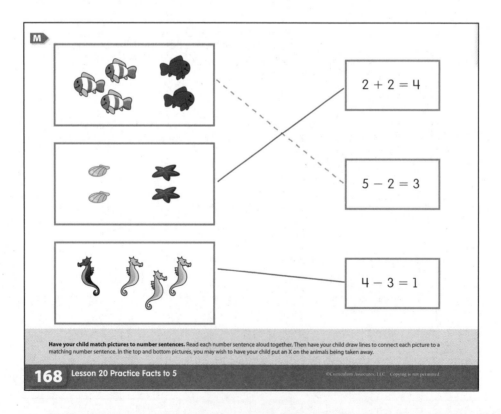

$2 + 2 = 4$

$5 - 2 = 3$

$4 - 3 = 1$

Have your child match pictures to number sentences. Read each number sentence aloud together. Then have your child draw lines to connect each picture to a matching number sentence. In the top and bottom pictures, you may wish to have your child put an X on the animals being taken away.

168   Lesson 20 Practice Facts to 5   ©Curriculum Associates, LLC   Copying is not permitted.

You may wish to assign the following pages for practice after completing the first Guided Practice in **Ready Mathematics**.

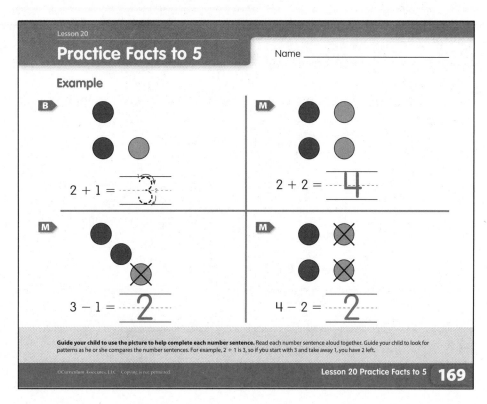

Lesson 20

Practice Facts to 5

Name _____

Example

B

$2 + 1 = 3$

M

$2 + 2 = 4$

M

$3 - 1 = 2$

M

$4 - 2 = 2$

Guide your child to use the picture to help complete each number sentence. Read each number sentence aloud together. Guide your child to look for patterns as he or she compares the number sentences. For example, 2 + 1 is 3, so if you start with 3 and take away 1, you have 2 left.

©Curriculum Associates, LLC   Copying is not permitted.

Lesson 20 Practice Facts to 5   **169**

Key

B Basic

M Medium

C Challenge

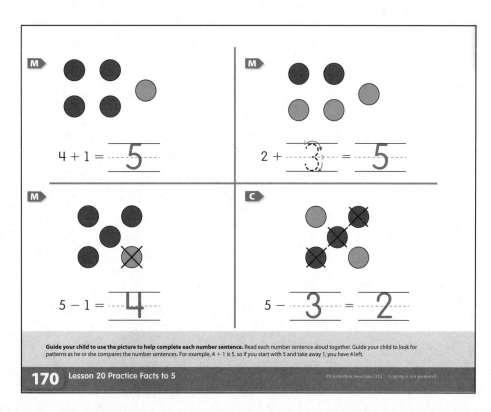

M

$4 + 1 = 5$

M

$2 + 3 = 5$

M

$5 - 1 = 4$

C

$5 - 3 = 2$

Guide your child to use the picture to help complete each number sentence. Read each number sentence aloud together. Guide your child to look for patterns as he or she compares the number sentences. For example, 4 + 1 is 5, so if you start with 5 and take away 1, you have 4 left.

170   Lesson 20 Practice Facts to 5

©Curriculum Associates, LLC   Copying is not permitted.

You may wish to assign the following pages for practice after completing the second Guided Practice in **Ready Mathematics.**

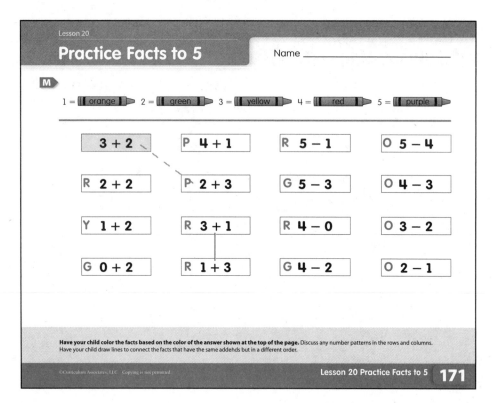

Lesson 20

Practice Facts to 5

Name _____

M

1 = orange 2 = green 3 = yellow 4 = red 5 = purple

3 + 2	P 4 + 1	R 5 − 1	O 5 − 4
R 2 + 2	P 2 + 3	G 5 − 3	O 4 − 3
Y 1 + 2	R 3 + 1	R 4 − 0	O 3 − 2
G 0 + 2	R 1 + 3	G 4 − 2	O 2 − 1

Have your child color the facts based on the color of the answer shown at the top of the page. Discuss any number patterns in the rows and columns. Have your child draw lines to connect the facts that have the same addehds but in a different order.

©Curriculum Associates, LLC Copying is not permitted.

Lesson 20 Practice Facts to 5 **171**

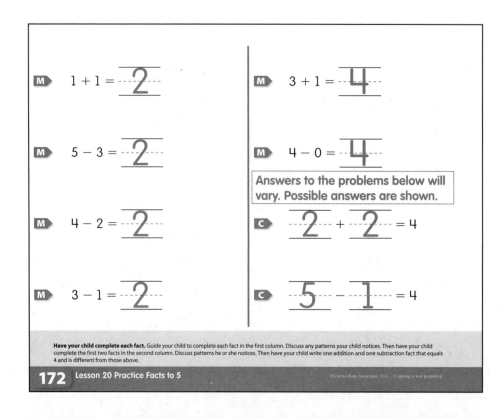

M 1 + 1 = 2

M 3 + 1 = 4

M 5 − 3 = 2

M 4 − 0 = 4

Answers to the problems below will vary. Possible answers are shown.

M 4 − 2 = 2

C 2 + 2 = 4

M 3 − 1 = 2

C 5 − 1 = 4

Have your child complete each fact. Guide your child to complete each fact in the first column. Discuss any patterns your child notices. Then have your child complete the first two facts in the second column. Discuss patterns he or she notices. Then have your child write one addition and one subtraction fact that equals 4 and is different from those above.

172 Lesson 20 Practice Facts to 5

©Curriculum Associates, LLC Copying is not permitted.

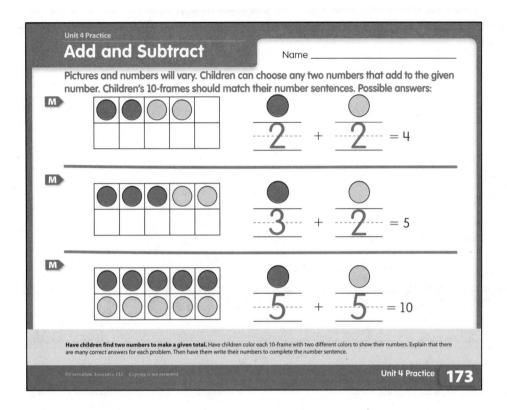

Unit 4 Practice
Add and Subtract

Name _____

Pictures and numbers will vary. Children can choose any two numbers that add to the given number. Children's 10-frames should match their number sentences. Possible answers:

M ▸

$$2 + 2 = 4$$

M ▸

$$3 + 2 = 5$$

M ▸

$$5 + 5 = 10$$

Have children find two numbers to make a given total. Have children color each 10-frame with two different colors to show their numbers. Explain that there are many correct answers for each problem. Then have them write their numbers to complete the number sentence.

©Curriculum Associates, LLC   Copying is not permitted.   Unit 4 Practice **173**

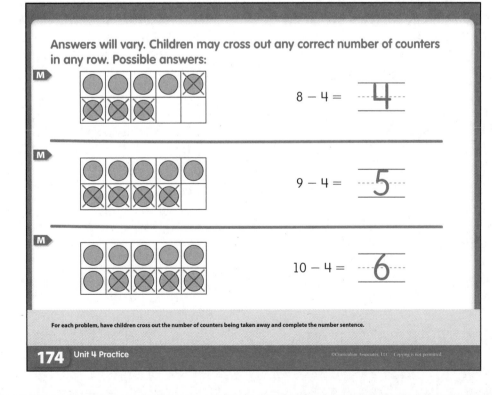

Answers will vary. Children may cross out any correct number of counters in any row. Possible answers:

M ▸

$$8 - 4 = 4$$

M ▸

$$9 - 4 = 5$$

M ▸

$$10 - 4 = 6$$

For each problem, have children cross out the number of counters being taken away and complete the number sentence.

174 Unit 4 Practice   ©Curriculum Associates, LLC   Copying is not permitted.

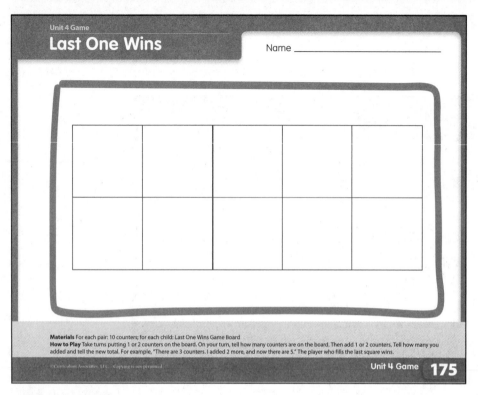

Unit 4 Game

Last One Wins

Name _____

Materials For each pair: 10 counters; for each child: Last One Wins Game Board
How to Play Take turns putting 1 or 2 counters on the board. On your turn, tell how many counters are on the board. Then add 1 or 2 counters. Tell how many you added and tell the new total. For example, "There are 3 counters. I added 2 more, and now there are 5." The player who fills the last square wins.

©Curriculum Associates, LLC Copying is not permitted.

Unit 4 Game **175**

STEP BY STEP

CCSS Focus - K.OA.A.1 *Embedded SMPs* - 1, 2, 6, 7 **Objective:** Understand addition. Add within 10.	**Materials:** For each pair: 10 counters, game board; for each child: recording sheet (optional)

• **Take turns putting 1 or 2 counters on the board. On your turn, tell how many counters are on the board. Then add 1 or 2 counters. Say how many you added and tell the new total.** Read the first four sentences of the *How to Play* aloud. After each step, ask children to explain in their own words what to do.

• **For example, "There are 3 counters. I added 2 more, and now there are 5." The player who fills the last square wins.** Finish reading *How to Play*, making sure children understand the rules and how to complete the game.

• Model the example from the directions. Display a 10-frame with 2 counters in it. Then add 2 more counters. Point to the counters as you describe what you did. You may want to model two or three turns and discuss strategies for deciding how many counters to add.

• To practice writing addition sentences, use the optional recording sheet (Teacher Resource 9). Have children record each move by writing a number sentence to show how many counters there were before, how many they added, and how many there are after.

Vary the Game To practice subtraction, start with the board filled with 10 counters. On each turn, have children take away 1 or 2 counters. The player who takes the last counter wins.

Challenge Use two 10-frames and play to 20 with either addition or subtraction.

You may wish to assign the following pages for practice after completing the Modeled Instruction in **Ready Mathematics.**

Lesson 21

Understand Teen Numbers

Name _____

What are teen numbers?

Check that children have colored the first 10 cubes red and 3 more cubes blue.

11   12   (13)   14   15   16   17   18   19

Have your child color the first 10 cubes red. Then have your child color 3 more cubes blue and circle the total number of colored cubes.

©Curriculum Associates, LLC   Copying is not permitted.

Lesson 21 *Understand* Teen Numbers   **179**

What are teen numbers?

Check that children have colored the first 10 cubes red and the rest of the cubes another color.

11   12   13   14   (15)   16   17   18   19

Have your child color the first 10 cubes red. Then have your child color the "extras" a different color. Have your child circle the total number of colored cubes.

180   Lesson 21 *Understand* Teen Numbers

©Curriculum Associates, LLC   Copying is not permitted.

You may wish to assign the following pages for practice after completing the Guided Exploration in ***Ready Mathematics.***

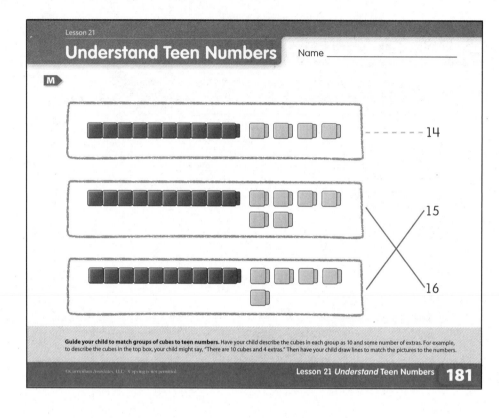

Lesson 21

Understand Teen Numbers   Name _____

M

14

15

16

Guide your child to match groups of cubes to teen numbers. Have your child describe the cubes in each group as 10 and some number of extras. For example, to describe the cubes in the top box, your child might say, "There are 10 cubes and 4 extras." Then have your child draw lines to match the pictures to the numbers.

©Curriculum Associates, LLC   Copying is not permitted.   Lesson 21 *Understand* Teen Numbers   **181**

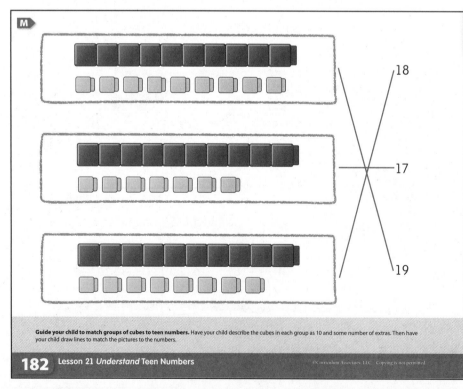

M

18

17

19

Guide your child to match groups of cubes to teen numbers. Have your child describe the cubes in each group as 10 and some number of extras. Then have your child draw lines to match the pictures to the numbers.

182   Lesson 21 *Understand* Teen Numbers   ©Curriculum Associates, LLC   Copying is not permitted.

You may wish to assign the following pages for practice after completing the Guided Practice in **Ready Mathematics.**

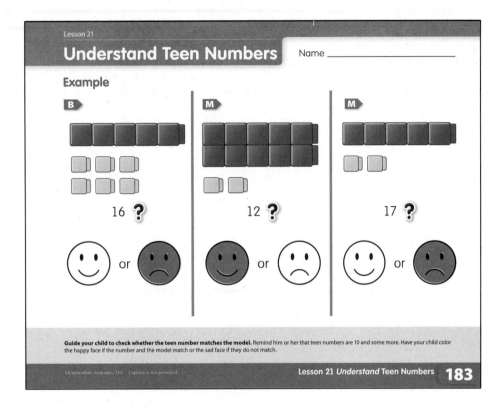

Lesson 21
Understand Teen Numbers   Name _____

Example

B

M

M

16 ❓

12 ❓

17 ❓

😊 or ☹️   😊 or 🙂   🙂 or ☹️

Guide your child to check whether the teen number matches the model. Remind him or her that teen numbers are 10 and some more. Have your child color the happy face if the number and the model match or the sad face if they do not match.

©Curriculum Associates, LLC   Copying is not permitted.

Lesson 21 *Understand* **Teen Numbers**   **183**

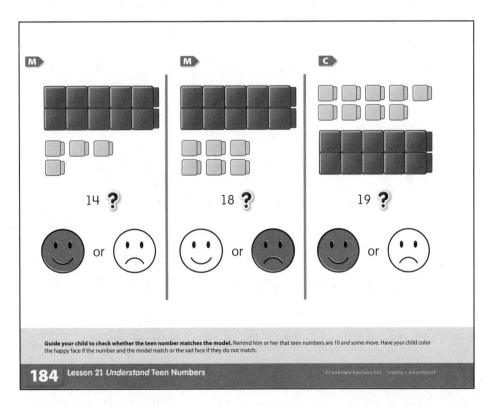

M

M

C

14 ❓

18 ❓

19 ❓

😊 or 🙂   🙂 or ☹️   😊 or ☹️

Guide your child to check whether the teen number matches the model. Remind him or her that teen numbers are 10 and some more. Have your child color the happy face if the number and the model match or the sad face if they do not match.

184   **Lesson 21** *Understand* **Teen Numbers**   ©Curriculum Associates, LLC   Copying is not permitted.

You may wish to assign the following pages for practice after completing the Modeled Instruction in *Ready Mathematics.*

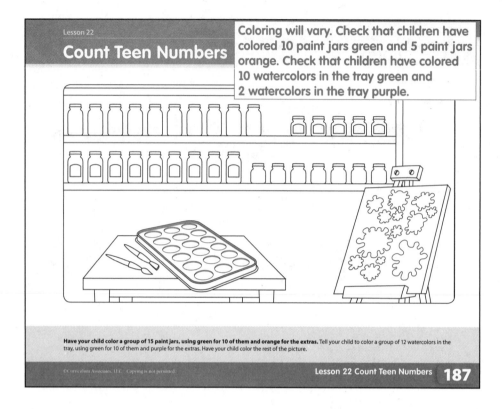

Lesson 22

Count Teen Numbers

Coloring will vary. Check that children have colored 10 paint jars green and 5 paint jars orange. Check that children have colored 10 watercolors in the tray green and 2 watercolors in the tray purple.

Have your child color a group of 15 paint jars, using green for 10 of them and orange for the extras. Tell your child to color a group of 12 watercolors in the tray, using green for 10 of them and purple for the extras. Have your child color the rest of the picture.

©Curriculum Associates, LLC   Copying is not permitted.

Lesson 22 Count Teen Numbers **187**

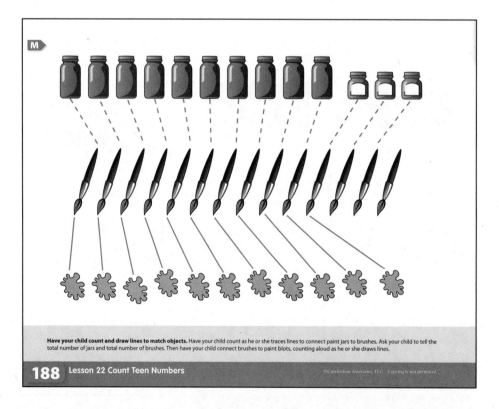

M

Have your child count and draw lines to match objects. Have your child count as he or she traces lines to connect paint jars to brushes. Ask your child to tell the total number of jars and total number of brushes. Then have your child connect brushes to paint blots, counting aloud as he or she draws lines.

188 Lesson 22 Count Teen Numbers

©Curriculum Associates, LLC   Copying is not permitted.

Unit 5 Counting and Cardinality, Numbers 11–100 and Number and Operations in Base Ten

You may wish to assign the following pages for practice after completing the first Guided Practice in *Ready Mathematics*.

Lesson 22
Count Teen Numbers

Children's circling may vary. Check that children have circled 10 objects in each problem.

Example

B

14
15
16

M

11
12
13

13

Guide your child to count teen numbers. Have your child count the objects in each problem. Then have him or her write the number counted. Have your child check his or her answer by circling a group of 10 objects and then counting the "extras."

©Curriculum Associates, LLC   Copying is not permitted.

Lesson 22 Count Teen Numbers **189**

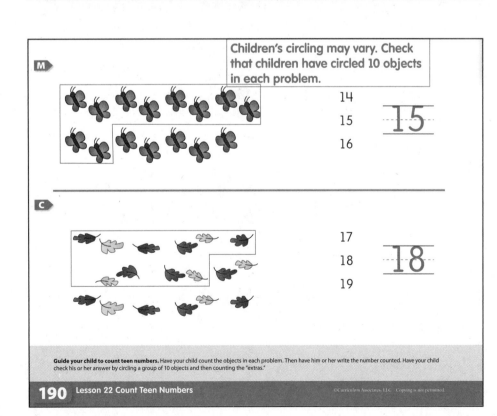

M

Children's circling may vary. Check that children have circled 10 objects in each problem.

14
15
16

15

C

17
18
19

18

Guide your child to count teen numbers. Have your child count the objects in each problem. Then have him or her write the number counted. Have your child check his or her answer by circling a group of 10 objects and then counting the "extras."

190 **Lesson 22 Count Teen Numbers**   ©Curriculum Associates, LLC   Copying is not permitted.

Key	
B	Basic
M	Medium
C	Challenge

You may wish to assign the following pages for practice after completing the second Guided Practice in *Ready Mathematics*.

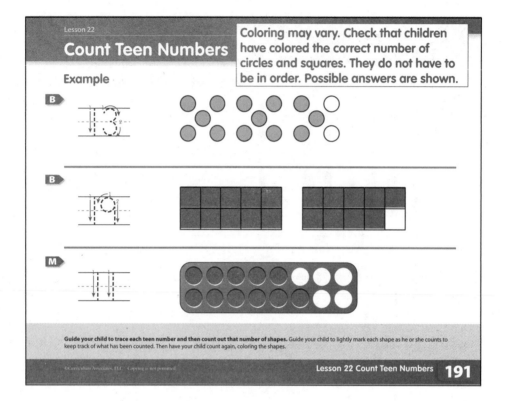

Lesson 22

Count Teen Numbers

Example

Coloring may vary. Check that children have colored the correct number of circles and squares. They do not have to be in order. Possible answers are shown.

Guide your child to trace each teen number and then count out that number of shapes. Guide your child to lightly mark each shape as he or she counts to keep track of what has been counted. Then have your child count again, coloring the shapes.

©Curriculum Associates, LLC Copying is not permitted.

Lesson 22 Count Teen Numbers 191

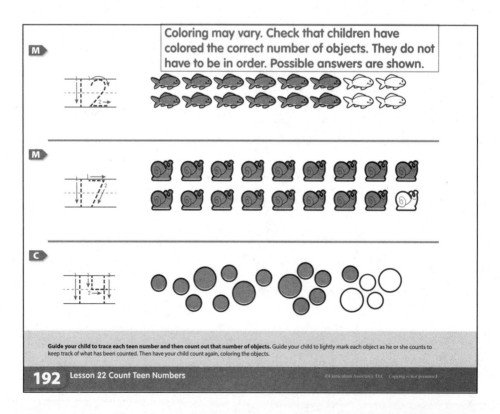

Coloring may vary. Check that children have colored the correct number of objects. They do not have to be in order. Possible answers are shown.

Guide your child to trace each teen number and then count out that number of objects. Guide your child to lightly mark each object as he or she counts to keep track of what has been counted. Then have your child count again, coloring the objects.

192 **Lesson 22 Count Teen Numbers**

©Curriculum Associates, LLC Copying is not permitted.

Unit 5 Counting and Cardinality, Numbers 11–100 and Number and Operations in Base Ten

You may wish to assign the following pages for practice after completing the Modeled Instruction in *Ready Mathematics.*

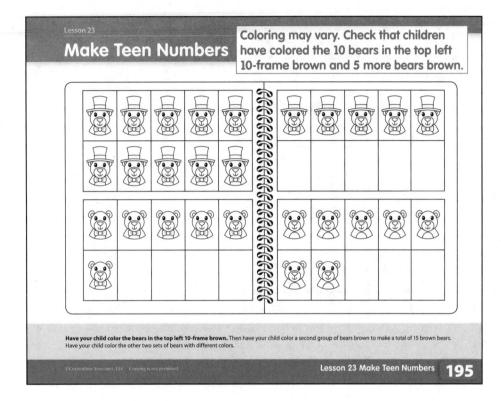

Lesson 23

Make Teen Numbers

Coloring may vary. Check that children have colored the 10 bears in the top left 10-frame brown and 5 more bears brown.

Have your child color the bears in the top left 10-frame brown. Then have your child color a second group of bears brown to make a total of 15 brown bears. Have your child color the other two sets of bears with different colors.

©Curriculum Associates, LLC   Copying is not permitted.

Lesson 23 Make Teen Numbers **195**

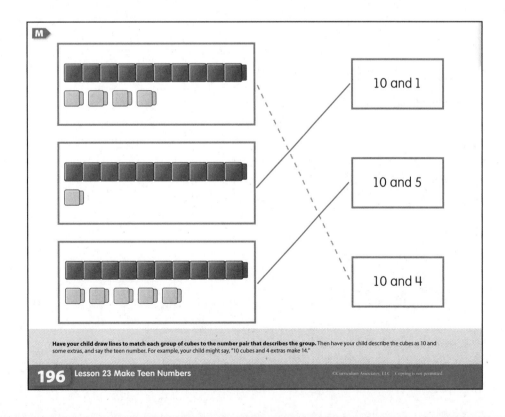

10 and 1

10 and 5

10 and 4

Have your child draw lines to match each group of cubes to the number pair that describes the group. Then have your child describe the cubes as 10 and some extras, and say the teen number. For example, your child might say, "10 cubes and 4 extras make 14."

196 Lesson 23 Make Teen Numbers

©Curriculum Associates, LLC   Copying is not permitted.

You may wish to assign the following pages for practice after completing the first Guided Practice in *Ready Mathematics*.

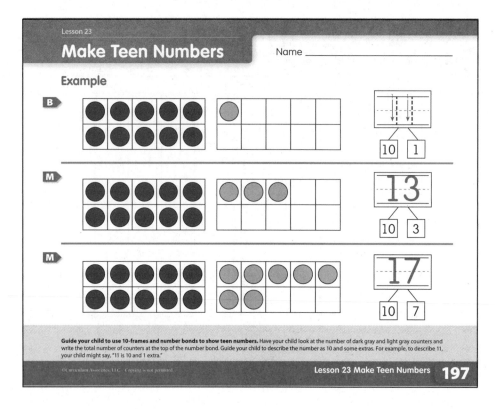

Lesson 23 Make Teen Numbers **197**

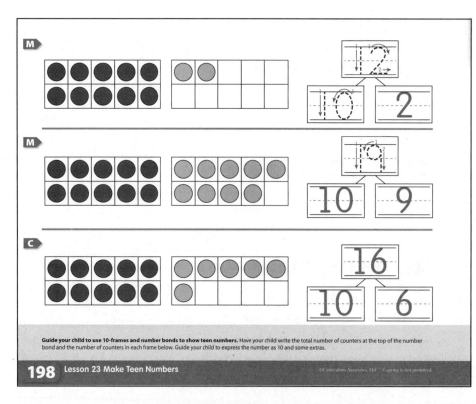

Key

B Basic

M Medium

C Challenge

198 Lesson 23 Make Teen Numbers

You may wish to assign the following pages for practice after completing the second Guided Practice in **Ready Mathematics.**

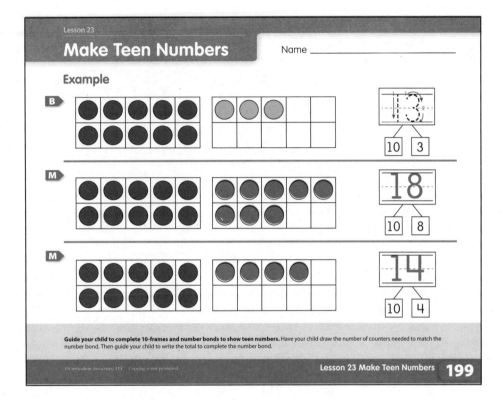

Lesson 23

Make Teen Numbers

Name _____

Example

Guide your child to complete 10-frames and number bonds to show teen numbers. Have your child draw the number of counters needed to match the number bond. Then guide your child to write the total to complete the number bond.

©Curriculum Associates, LLC   Copying is not permitted.

Lesson 23 Make Teen Numbers **199**

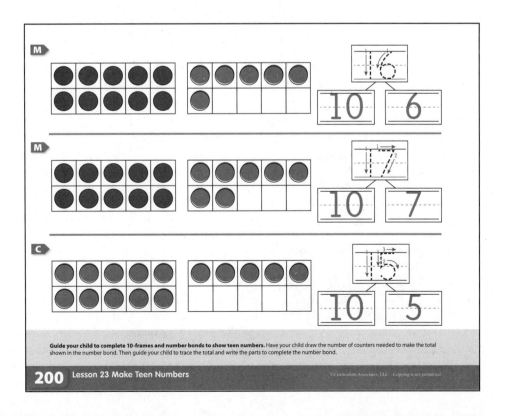

Guide your child to complete 10-frames and number bonds to show teen numbers. Have your child draw the number of counters needed to make the total shown in the number bond. Then guide your child to trace the total and write the parts to complete the number bond.

200 Lesson 23 Make Teen Numbers

©Curriculum Associates, LLC   Copying is not permitted.

You may wish to assign the following pages for practice after completing the Modeled Instruction in *Ready Mathematics*.

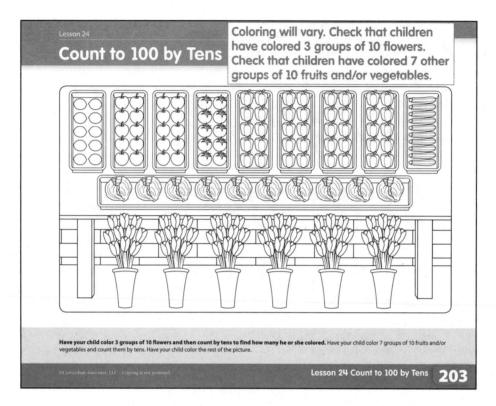

Lesson 24

Count to 100 by Tens

Coloring will vary. Check that children have colored 3 groups of 10 flowers. Check that children have colored 7 other groups of 10 fruits and/or vegetables.

Have your child color 3 groups of 10 flowers and then count by tens to find how many he or she colored. Have your child color 7 groups of 10 fruits and/or vegetables and count them by tens. Have your child color the rest of the picture.

©Curriculum Associates, LLC Copying is not permitted.   Lesson 24 Count to 100 by Tens **203**

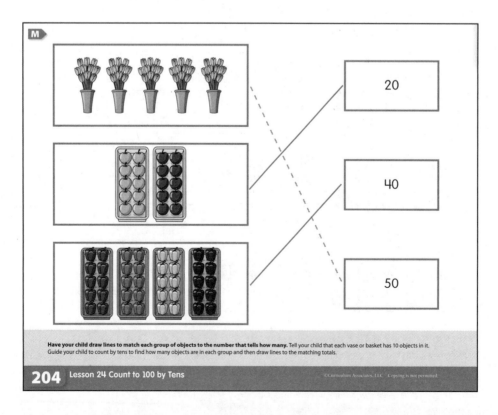

M

20

40

50

Have your child draw lines to match each group of objects to the number that tells how many. Tell your child that each vase or basket has 10 objects in it. Guide your child to count by tens to find how many objects are in each group and then draw lines to the matching totals.

204 Lesson 24 Count to 100 by Tens   ©Curriculum Associates, LLC Copying is not permitted.

You may wish to assign the following pages for practice after completing the first Guided Practice in *Ready Mathematics*.

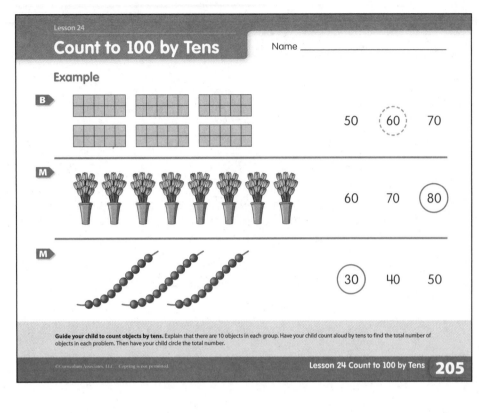

Lesson 24

Count to 100 by Tens

Name _____

Example

B ▸   50   (60)   70

M ▸   60   70   (80)

M ▸   (30)   40   50

Guide your child to count objects by tens. Explain that there are 10 objects in each group. Have your child count aloud by tens to find the total number of objects in each problem. Then have your child circle the total number.

©Curriculum Associates, LLC   Copying is not permitted.   Lesson 24 Count to 100 by Tens   **205**

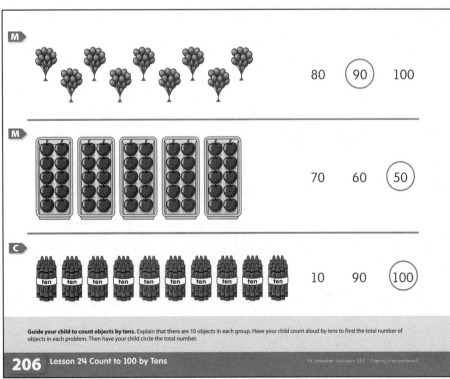

M ▸   80   (90)   100

M ▸   70   60   (50)

C ▸   10   90   (100)

Guide your child to count objects by tens. Explain that there are 10 objects in each group. Have your child count aloud by tens to find the total number of objects in each problem. Then have your child circle the total number.

206   Lesson 24 Count to 100 by Tens   ©Curriculum Associates, LLC   Copying is not permitted.

You may wish to assign the following pages for practice after completing the second Guided Practice in *Ready Mathematics*.

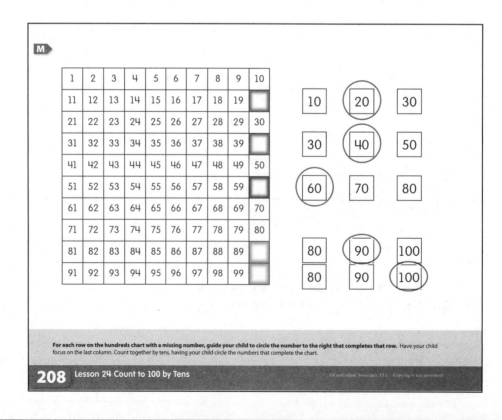

Lesson 24

Count to 100 by Tens

Name _____

M

1	2	3	4	5	6	7	8	9	☐
11	12	13	14	15	16	17	18	19	20
21	22	23	24	25	26	27	28	29	☐
31	32	33	34	35	36	37	38	39	40
41	42	43	44	45	46	47	48	49	50
51	52	53	54	55	56	57	58	59	60
61	62	63	64	65	66	67	68	69	☐
71	72	73	74	75	76	77	78	79	80
81	82	83	84	85	86	87	88	89	☐
91	92	93	94	95	96	97	98	99	100

10   20   30

30   40   50

60   70   80

70   80   90

For each row on the hundreds chart with a missing number, guide your child to circle the number to the right that completes that row. Have your child count aloud to 10 by ones to find which number completes the first row. Then guide your child to focus on the last column and count together by tens, having your child circle the numbers that complete the chart.

©Curriculum Associates, LLC Copying is not permitted.

Lesson 24 Count to 100 by Tens **207**

M

1	2	3	4	5	6	7	8	9	10
11	12	13	14	15	16	17	18	19	☐
21	22	23	24	25	26	27	28	29	30
31	32	33	34	35	36	37	38	39	☐
41	42	43	44	45	46	47	48	49	50
51	52	53	54	55	56	57	58	59	☐
61	62	63	64	65	66	67	68	69	70
71	72	73	74	75	76	77	78	79	80
81	82	83	84	85	86	87	88	89	☐
91	92	93	94	95	96	97	98	99	☐

10   20   30

30   40   50

60   70   80

80   90   100

80   90   100

For each row on the hundreds chart with a missing number, guide your child to circle the number to the right that completes that row. Have your child focus on the last column. Count together by tens, having your child circle the numbers that complete the chart.

208 Lesson 24 Count to 100 by Tens   ©Curriculum Associates, LLC Copying is not permitted.

You may wish to assign the following pages for practice after completing the Modeled Instruction in **Ready Mathematics**.

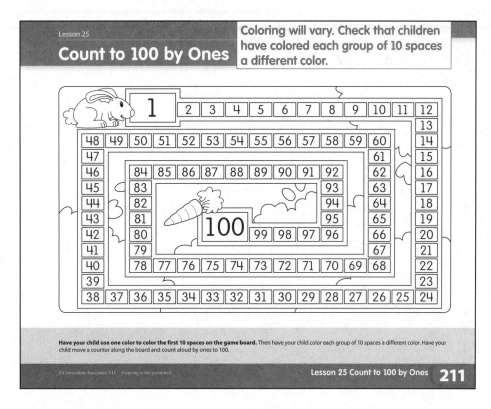

Lesson 25

Count to 100 by Ones

Coloring will vary. Check that children have colored each group of 10 spaces a different color.

Have your child use one color to color the first 10 spaces on the game board. Then have your child color each group of 10 spaces a different color. Have your child move a counter along the board and count aloud by ones to 100.

©Curriculum Associates, LLC   Copying is not permitted.   Lesson 25 Count to 100 by Ones **211**

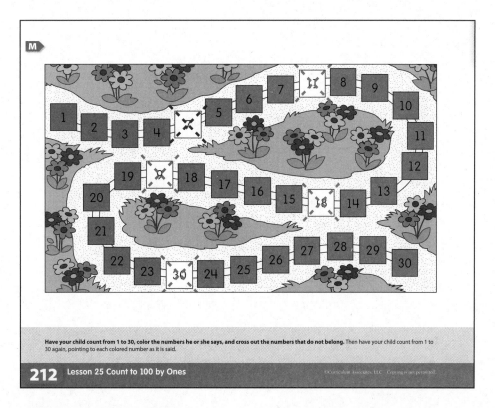

Have your child count from 1 to 30, color the numbers he or she says, and cross out the numbers that do not belong. Then have your child count from 1 to 30 again, pointing to each colored number as it is said.

212 Lesson 25 Count to 100 by Ones   ©Curriculum Associates, LLC   Copying is not permitted.

You may wish to assign the following pages for practice after completing the first Guided Practice in *Ready Mathematics.*

Lesson 25

Count to 100 by Ones   Name _____

M ▶

1	2	3	4	5	6	7	8	9	10
11	12	13	14	15	16	17	18	19	20
21	22	23	24		26	27	28	29	30
31	32	33	34	35	36	37	38	39	40
41	42		44	45	46	47	48	49	50
	52	53	54	55	56	57	58	59	60
61	62	63	64	65	66	67	68	69	70
71	72	73	74	75	76	77	78	79	
81	82	83	84	85	86		88	89	90
91	92	93	94	95	96	97	98	99	100

(25)   26   35

42   (43)   44
(51)   60   61

60   70   (80)
(87)   88   96

For each row on the hundreds chart with a missing number, guide your child to circle the number to the right that completes that row. Count aloud by ones together until you get to the first empty box. Help your child find the missing number to the right of the hundreds chart and circle it. Count on together until you reach the next empty box, and repeat the process.

Lesson 25 Count to 100 by Ones **213**

M ▶

1	2	3	4	5	6	7	8	9	10
11	12	13	14	15	16	17	18	19	20
21	22	23	24	25	26	27		29	30
31	32	33	34	35	36	37	38	39	40
41	42	43	44	45	46	47	48	49	50
51		53	54	55	56	57	58	59	60
61	62	63	64	65		67	68	69	70
71	72	73	74	75	76	77	78	79	80
81	82	83	84	85	86	87	88	89	
	92	93	94	95	96	97	98	99	100

8   26   (28)

(52)   53   62
(66)   70   75

80   (90)   91
82   90   (91)

For each row on the hundreds chart with a missing number, guide your child to circle the number to the right that completes that row. Count aloud by ones together until you get to the first empty box. Help your child find the missing number to the right of the hundreds chart and circle it. Count on together until you reach the next empty box, and repeat the process.

214 Lesson 25 Count to 100 by Ones

Key

B Basic

M Medium

C Challenge

You may wish to assign the following pages for practice after completing the second Guided Practice in *Ready Mathematics*.

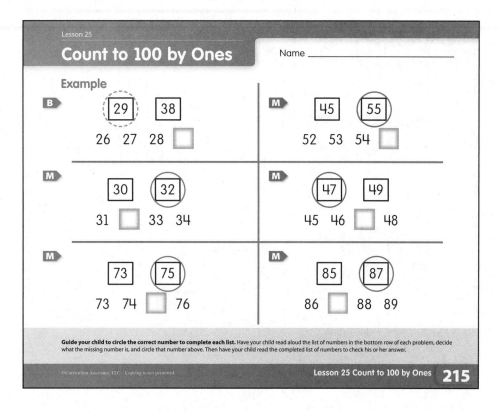

Lesson 25

Count to 100 by Ones

Name _____

Example

B ▶ (29) 38
26 27 28 ☐

M ▶ 45 (55)
52 53 54 ☐

M ▶ 30 (32)
31 ☐ 33 34

M ▶ (47) 49
45 46 ☐ 48

M ▶ 73 (75)
73 74 ☐ 76

M ▶ 85 (87)
86 ☐ 88 89

Guide your child to circle the correct number to complete each list. Have your child read aloud the list of numbers in the bottom row of each problem, decide what the missing number is, and circle that number above. Then have your child read the completed list of numbers to check his or her answer.

©Curriculum Associates, LLC Copying is not permitted.

Lesson 25 Count to 100 by Ones **215**

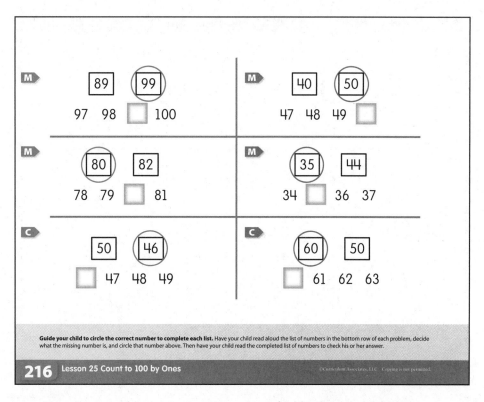

M ▶ 89 (99)
97 98 ☐ 100

M ▶ 40 (50)
47 48 49 ☐

M ▶ (80) 82
78 79 ☐ 81

M ▶ (35) 44
34 ☐ 36 37

C ▶ 50 (46)
☐ 47 48 49

C ▶ (60) 50
☐ 61 62 63

Guide your child to circle the correct number to complete each list. Have your child read aloud the list of numbers in the bottom row of each problem, decide what the missing number is, and circle that number above. Then have your child read the completed list of numbers to check his or her answer.

216 Lesson 25 Count to 100 by Ones

©Curriculum Associates, LLC Copying is not permitted.

Unit 5 Practice
Numbers 11 to 100

Name _____

M

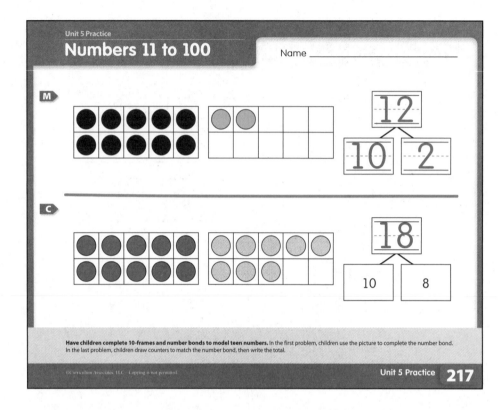

12
10 2

C

18
10 8

Have children complete 10-frames and number bonds to model teen numbers. In the first problem, children use the picture to complete the number bond. In the last problem, children draw counters to match the number bond, then write the total.

Unit 5 Practice **217**

M   30 (40)

20 30 ____ 50

M   (60) 50

40 50 ____ 70

M   (40) 50

____ 50 60 70

M   60 (20)

____ 30 40 50

C   ☹ | 37 | 38 | 39 | 40 | 41 | ✗ | 42 |

Have children count by tens, then by ones. For the first four problems, ask children to circle the number that completes the lists as they count by tens. For the last problem, have children cross out the box that shows the incorrect number as they count by ones.

218 Unit 5 Practice

Unit 5 Game
Teen Number Cover-Up
Name _____

11	12	13
14	15	16
17	18	19

Materials For each pair: Teen Number Picture Cards; for each child: Teen Number Cover-Up Game Board
How to Play Take a card and tell the number it shows. Put it on a matching number square on the game board. If the card does not show a teen number, do not cover a square. If the number is already covered, skip a turn. The first player to cover all the squares wins.

Unit 5 Game　**219**

STEP BY STEP

CCSS Focus - K.CC.A.3, K.CC.B.5, K.NBT.A.1 *Embedded SMPs -* 1, 2, 7, 8 **Objective:** Understand teen numbers as 10 and some extras. Match teen numbers with various representations that show ten and some ones.	**Materials:** For each pair: Teen Number Picture Cards (Teacher Resource 11); for each child: game board

- **Take a card and tell the number it shows. Put it on a matching number square on the game board. If the card does not show a teen number, do not cover a square.** Read the first three sentences of the *How to Play* aloud. After each step, ask children to explain in their own words what to do.

- **If the number is already covered, skip a turn. The first player to cover all the squares wins.** Finish reading *How to Play*, making sure children understand the rules and how to complete the game.

- Make a stack of cards. Model taking a card, and thinking aloud as you determine which number it matches. Encourage children to share strategies they would use to find the number shown on the card. Place the card on the matching square on the game board.

- You may also want to model taking a card that is not a teen number. Model deciding that there is no match on the game board. Place the card at the bottom of the stack when you are done.

- Observe as children play the game and note if children count the dots on the cards or if they are able to recognize the number visually.

Vary the Game Play with Teen Number Cards (Teacher Resource 12) instead of Teen Number Picture Cards to practice number recognition. As children match numbers, have them say the number names.

Extra Support Some children may need the support of concrete materials for counting. Allow them to use counters to represent and count the dots on the cards.

You may wish to assign the following pages for practice after completing the Modeled Instruction in *Ready Mathematics*.

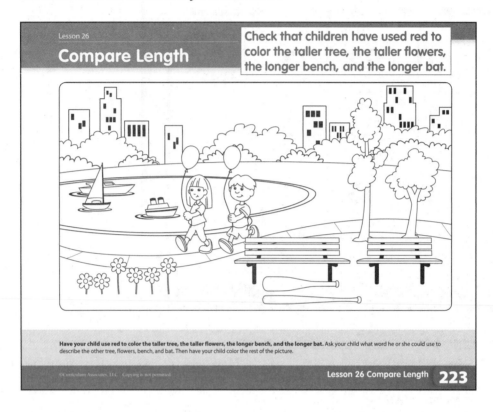

Lesson 26

Compare Length

Check that children have used red to color the taller tree, the taller flowers, the longer bench, and the longer bat.

Have your child use red to color the taller tree, the taller flowers, the longer bench, and the longer bat. Ask your child what word he or she could use to describe the other tree, flowers, bench, and bat. Then have your child color the rest of the picture.

©Curriculum Associates, LLC   Copying is not permitted.   Lesson 26 Compare Length **223**

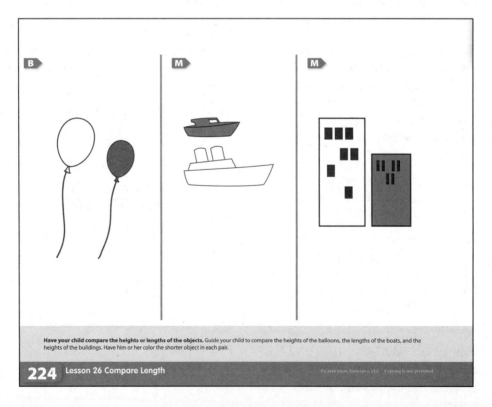

B   **M**   **M**

Have your child compare the heights or lengths of the objects. Guide your child to compare the heights of the balloons, the lengths of the boats, and the heights of the buildings. Have him or her color the shorter object in each pair.

224 Lesson 26 Compare Length   ©Curriculum Associates, LLC   Copying is not permitted.

You may wish to assign the following pages for practice after completing the first Guided Practice in *Ready Mathematics.*

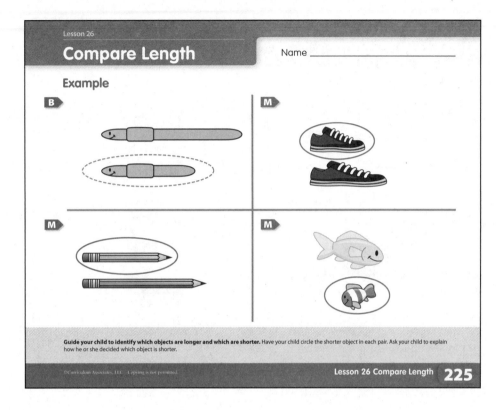

Lesson 26

Compare Length   Name _____

Example

Guide your child to identify which objects are longer and which are shorter. Have your child circle the shorter object in each pair. Ask your child to explain how he or she decided which object is shorter.

©Curriculum Associates, LLC Copying is not permitted.   Lesson 26 Compare Length **225**

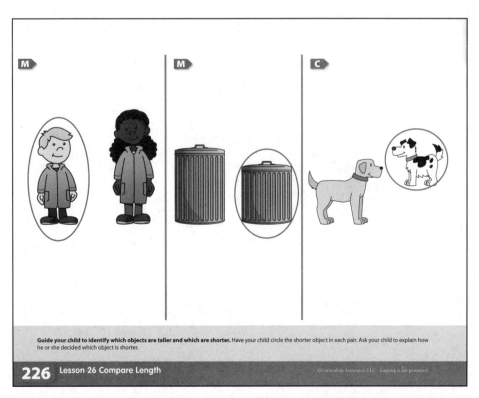

Guide your child to identify which objects are taller and which are shorter. Have your child circle the shorter object in each pair. Ask your child to explain how he or she decided which object is shorter.

226 Lesson 26 Compare Length   ©Curriculum Associates, LLC Copying is not permitted.

You may wish to assign the following pages for practice after completing the second Guided Practice in *Ready Mathematics.*

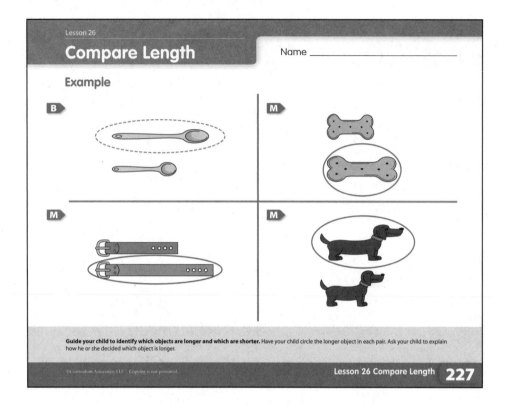

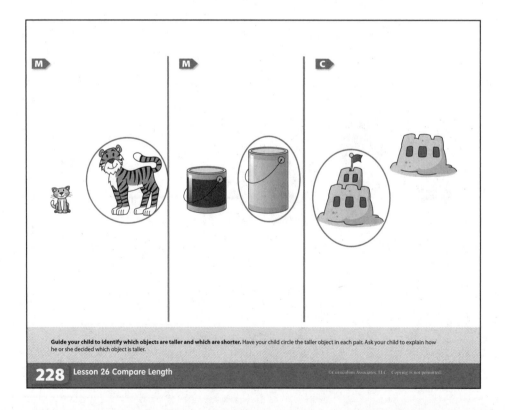

You may wish to assign the following pages for practice after completing the Modeled Instruction in *Ready Mathematics*.

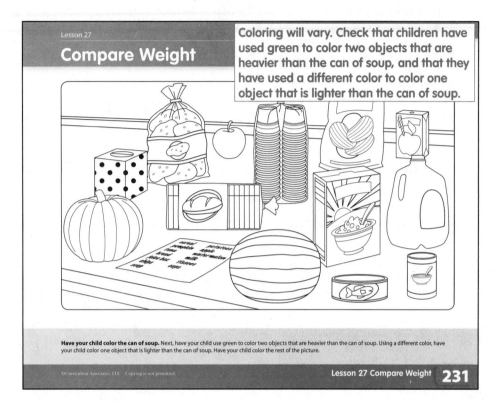

Lesson 27

Compare Weight

> Coloring will vary. Check that children have used green to color two objects that are heavier than the can of soup, and that they have used a different color to color one object that is lighter than the can of soup.

Have your child color the can of soup. Next, have your child use green to color two objects that are heavier than the can of soup. Using a different color, have your child color one object that is lighter than the can of soup. Have your child color the rest of the picture.

Lesson 27 Compare Weight **231**

> Check that children have circled the box of cereal, colored the watermelon and potatoes red, and colored the balloon, leaf, and flower blue.

Have your child circle the box of cereal. Have your child look for objects that are heavier than a box of cereal and color them red. Then have your child look for objects that are lighter than a box of cereal and color them blue.

232 Lesson 27 Compare Weight

You may wish to assign the following pages for practice after completing the first Guided Practice in *Ready Mathematics.*

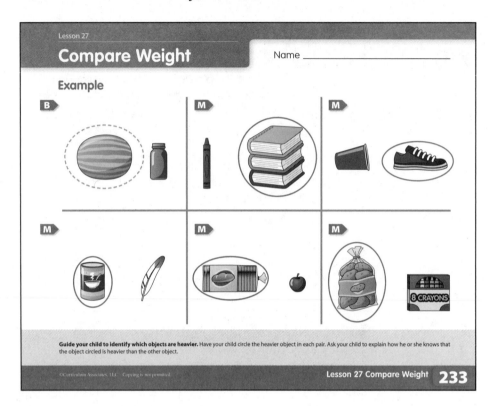

Lesson 27

Compare Weight   Name _____

Example

Guide your child to identify which objects are heavier. Have your child circle the heavier object in each pair. Ask your child to explain how he or she knows that the object circled is heavier than the other object.

©Curriculum Associates, LLC   Copying is not permitted.   **Lesson 27 Compare Weight** **233**

Key

B Basic

M Medium

C Challenge

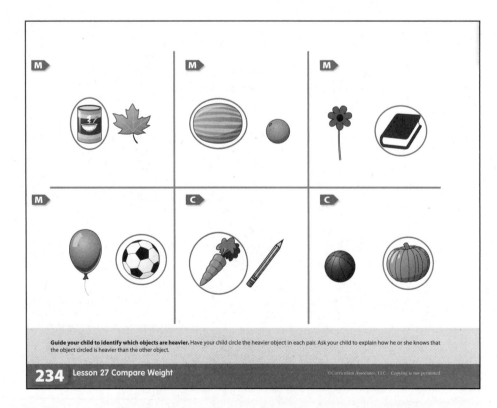

Guide your child to identify which objects are heavier. Have your child circle the heavier object in each pair. Ask your child to explain how he or she knows that the object circled is heavier than the other object.

234 Lesson 27 Compare Weight   ©Curriculum Associates, LLC   Copying is not permitted.

You may wish to assign the following pages for practice after completing the second Guided Practice in *Ready Mathematics.*

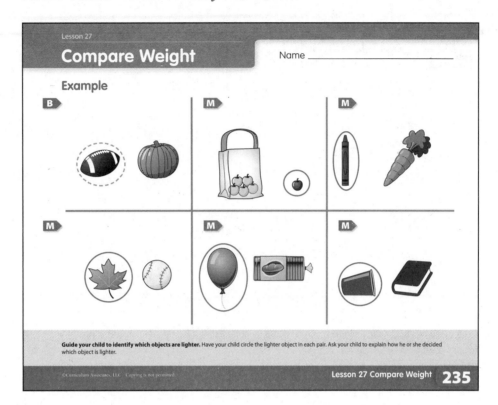

Lesson 27

Compare Weight

Name _____

Example

Guide your child to identify which objects are lighter. Have your child circle the lighter object in each pair. Ask your child to explain how he or she decided which object is lighter.

©Curriculum Associates, LLC   Copying is not permitted.

Lesson 27 Compare Weight **235**

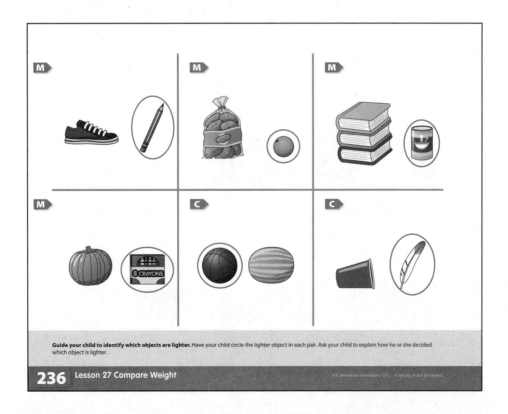

Guide your child to identify which objects are lighter. Have your child circle the lighter object in each pair. Ask your child to explain how he or she decided which object is lighter.

236 Lesson 27 Compare Weight

©Curriculum Associates, LLC   Copying is not permitted.

You may wish to assign the following pages for practice after completing the Modeled Instruction in **Ready Mathematics.**

Lesson 28

Sort Objects

Check that your child colored the 4 striped fish red and the other 11 fish yellow.

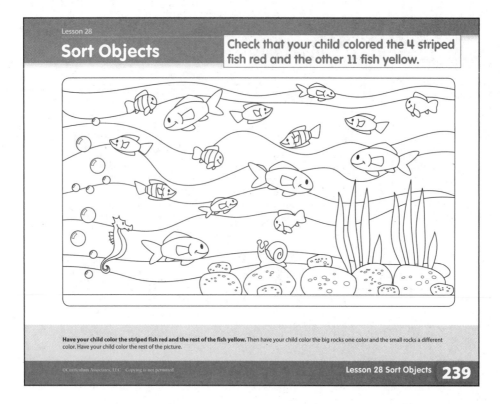

Have your child color the striped fish red and the rest of the fish yellow. Then have your child color the big rocks one color and the small rocks a different color. Have your child color the rest of the picture.

©Curriculum Associates, LLC   Copying is not permitted.   Lesson 28 Sort Objects **239**

There are 10 objects that are colored and 7 objects that are not.

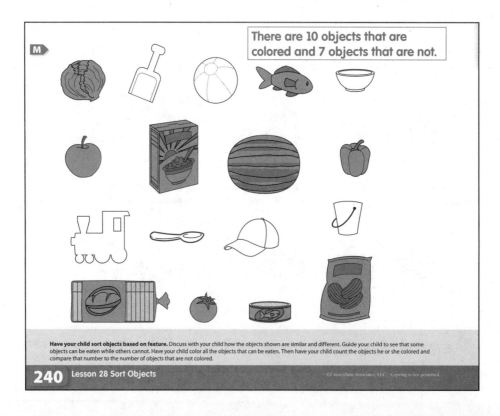

Have your child sort objects based on feature. Discuss with your child how the objects shown are similar and different. Guide your child to see that some objects can be eaten while others cannot. Have your child color all the objects that can be eaten. Then have your child count the objects he or she colored and compare that number to the number of objects that are not colored.

240 Lesson 28 Sort Objects   ©Curriculum Associates, LLC   Copying is not permitted.

You may wish to assign the following pages for practice after completing the first Guided Practice in *Ready Mathematics*.

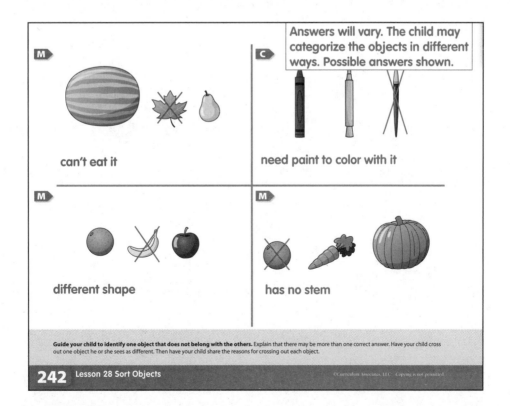

Answers will vary. The child may categorize the objects in different ways. Possible answers shown.

B

C

worn indoors

M

not a girl

M

has spots

Guide your child to identify one object that does not belong with the others. Explain that there may be more than one correct answer. Have your child cross out one object he or she sees as different. Then have your child share the reasons for crossing out each object.

©Curriculum Associates, LLC   Copying is not permitted.

Lesson 28 Sort Objects **241**

Key

B Basic
M Medium
C Challenge

M

Answers will vary. The child may categorize the objects in different ways. Possible answers shown.

C

can't eat it

need paint to color with it

M

different shape

M

has no stem

Guide your child to identify one object that does not belong with the others. Explain that there may be more than one correct answer. Have your child cross out one object he or she sees as different. Then have your child share the reasons for crossing out each object.

242 Lesson 28 Sort Objects

©Curriculum Associates, LLC   Copying is not permitted.

You may wish to assign the following pages for practice after completing the second Guided Practice in *Ready Mathematics.*

Lesson 28
Sort Objects

Name _____

Example

B ▸

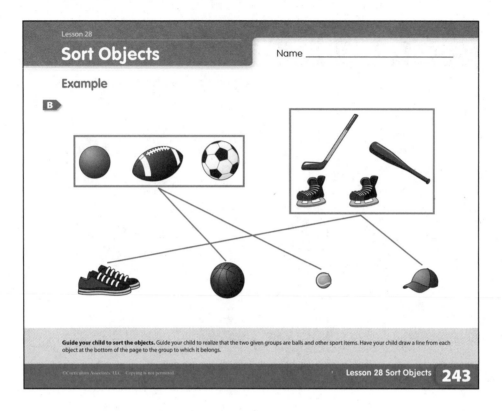

Guide your child to sort the objects. Guide your child to realize that the two given groups are balls and other sport items. Have your child draw a line from each object at the bottom of the page to the group to which it belongs.

©Curriculum Associates, LLC   Copying is not permitted.

Lesson 28 Sort Objects **243**

M ▸

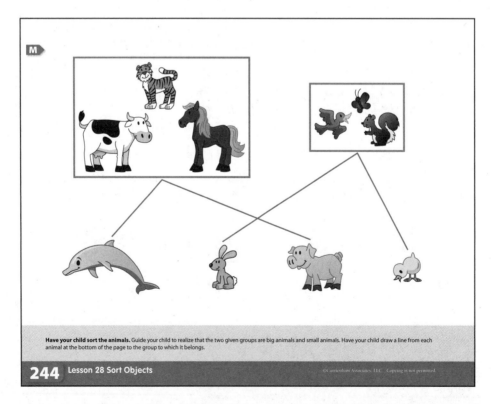

Have your child sort the animals. Guide your child to realize that the two given groups are big animals and small animals. Have your child draw a line from each animal at the bottom of the page to the group to which it belongs.

244 Lesson 28 Sort Objects

©Curriculum Associates, LLC   Copying is not permitted.

Unit 6 Practice
Compare and Sort

Name _____

Children's drawings will vary. Check that the crayon children draw is longer than the given crayon. Check that the object children draw is heavier than a juice box.

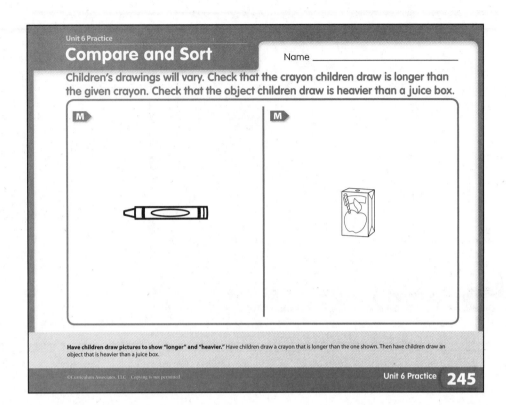

Have children draw pictures to show "longer" and "heavier." Have children draw a crayon that is longer than the one shown. Then have children draw an object that is heavier than a juice box.

Unit 6 Practice **245**

Key
B Basic
M Medium
C Challenge

Have children sort the fish by size. Have children find all the small fish and write how many. Then have them find all the big fish and write how many.

246 Unit 6 Practice

Unit 6 Game

Shorter and Longer

Name _____

Shorter

Same

Longer

Materials For each pair: 2 dot cubes (1–6); for each child: Shorter and Longer Game Board, 50 connecting cubes
How to Play Roll 2 dot cubes. Count the dots and build a train with that many cubes. If the train is shorter than the crayon, put it in the "shorter" box. If the train is longer, put it in the "longer" box. If it is the same length, put it in the "same" box. The first person to get 1 shorter train and 1 longer train wins.

©Curriculum Associates, LLC   Copying is not permitted.

Unit 6 Game **247**

STEP BY STEP

CCSS Focus - K.MD.A.2 *Embedded SMPs* - 1, 2, 7, 8 **Objective:** Compare the length of objects. Sort objects by length.	**Materials:** For each pair: 2 dot cubes (1–6); for each child: game board, 50 connecting cubes

- **Roll 2 dot cubes. Count the dots and build a train with that many cubes.** Read the first two sentences of the *How to Play* aloud. After each step, ask children to explain in their own words what to do.

- Model rolling two dot cubes, counting the dots, and making a cube train.

- **If the train is shorter than the crayon, put it in the "shorter" box. If the train is longer, put it in the "longer" box. If it is the same length, put it in the "same" box. The first person to get one shorter train and one longer train wins.** Finish reading *How to Play*, making sure children understand the rules and how to complete the game.

- Model comparing the length of the train to the crayon. First model incorrectly, by not aligning either end, and discuss the error. Then model correctly, and place the train in the proper box.

- When children build a train that belongs in a box that is already filled, have them say whether the train is shorter, the same, or longer than the crayon, then dismantle it.

- Circulate as children play the game. Ask questions, such as: *How many cubes are in a shorter train? How many cubes are in a longer train? About how many cubes long is the crayon?*

Vary the Game Let children choose classroom objects to compare to. Have children use different measuring tools, such as Measuring Strips (Teacher Resource 14) or paper clip chains. Tell them to find strips that are shorter, longer, and about the same length as the classroom objects.

Extra Support For children who struggle to count the dots on two dot cubes, use only one cube and choose a different object that is about 3 connecting cubes in length.

You may wish to assign the following pages for practice after completing the Modeled Instruction in *Ready Mathematics.*

Lesson 29
See Position and Shape

Check that children colored the correct objects.

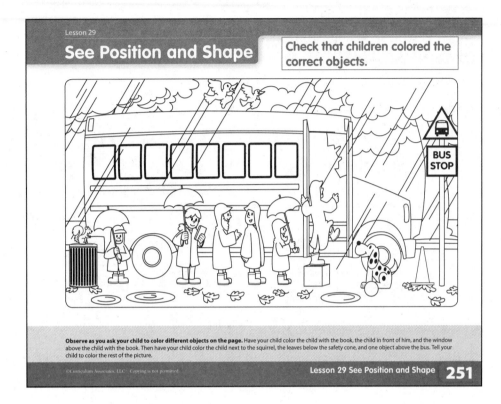

Observe as you ask your child to color different objects on the page. Have your child color the child with the book, the child in front of him, and the window above the child with the book. Then have your child color the child next to the squirrel, the leaves below the safety cone, and one object above the bus. Tell your child to color the rest of the picture.

©Curriculum Associates, LLC Copying is not permitted.

Lesson 29 See Position and Shape **251**

B

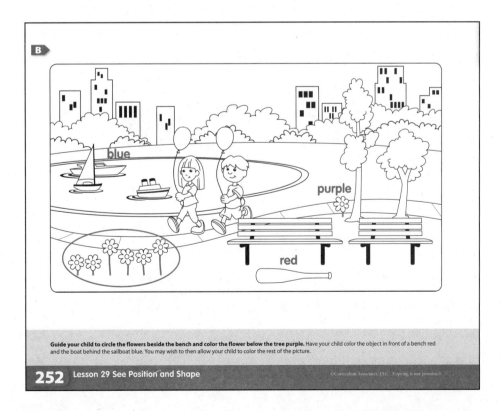

Guide your child to circle the flowers beside the bench and color the flower below the tree purple. Have your child color the object in front of a bench red and the boat behind the sailboat blue. You may wish to then allow your child to color the rest of the picture.

252 Lesson 29 See Position and Shape   ©Curriculum Associates, LLC Copying is not permitted.

You may wish to assign the following pages for practice after completing the first Guided Practice in *Ready Mathematics*.

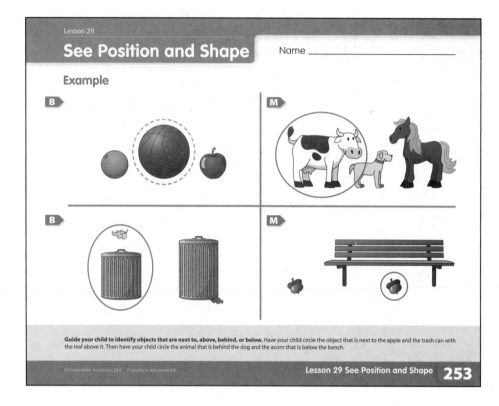

Lesson 29

See Position and Shape

Name _____

Example

Guide your child to identify objects that are next to, above, behind, or below. Have your child circle the object that is next to the apple and the trash can with the leaf above it. Then have your child circle the animal that is behind the dog and the acorn that is below the bench.

©Curriculum Associates, LLC Copying is not permitted.

Lesson 29 See Position and Shape **253**

Key

B Basic

M Medium

C Challenge

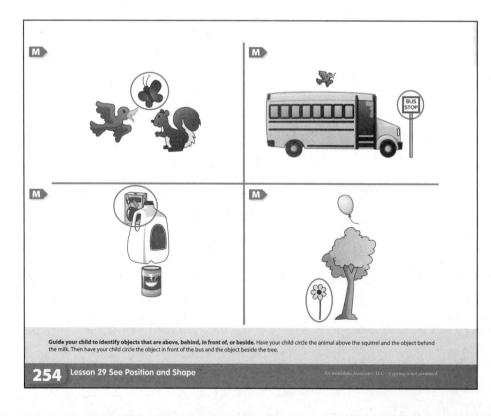

Guide your child to identify objects that are above, behind, in front of, or beside. Have your child circle the animal above the squirrel and the object behind the milk. Then have your child circle the object in front of the bus and the object beside the tree.

254 Lesson 29 See Position and Shape   ©Curriculum Associates, LLC Copying is not permitted.

You may wish to assign the following pages for practice after completing the second Guided Practice in *Ready Mathematics*.

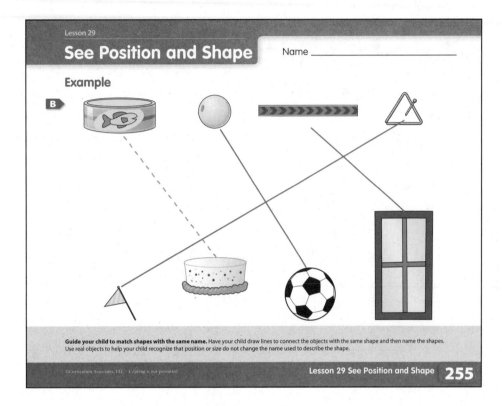

Lesson 29

See Position and Shape   Name _____

Example

B ▶

Guide your child to match shapes with the same name. Have your child draw lines to connect the objects with the same shape and then name the shapes. Use real objects to help your child recognize that position or size do not change the name used to describe the shape.

©Curriculum Associates, LLC Copying is not permitted.

Lesson 29 See Position and Shape   **255**

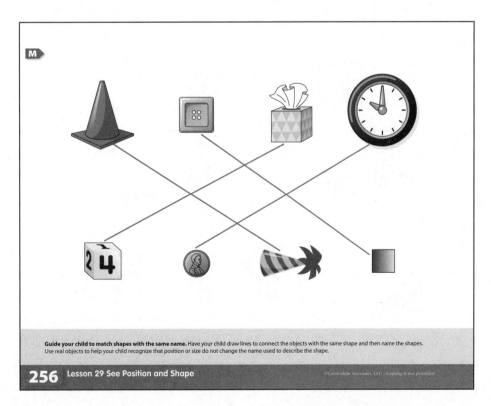

M ▶

Guide your child to match shapes with the same name. Have your child draw lines to connect the objects with the same shape and then name the shapes. Use real objects to help your child recognize that position or size do not change the name used to describe the shape.

256   Lesson 29 See Position and Shape   ©Curriculum Associates, LLC Copying is not permitted.

You may wish to assign the following pages for practice after completing the
Modeled Instruction in **Ready Mathematics.**

Lesson 30

Name Shapes

Check children's work. Possible
shapes are shown.

hexagon

square

circle

rectangle

TAXI

TAXI

TAXI

triangle

cone

cube

cylinder

sphere

Observe as you ask your child to color different shapes on the page. Have your child color a square, a rectangle, a circle, a triangle, and a hexagon. Then have
your child color a sphere, a cube, a cone, and a cylinder. Have your child color the rest of the picture.

©Curriculum Associates, LLC   Copying is not permitted.

Lesson 30 Name Shapes **259**

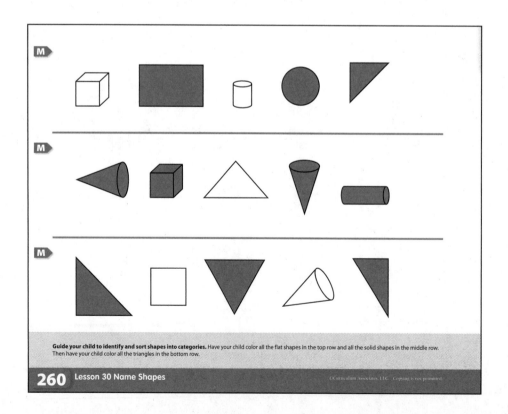

Guide your child to identify and sort shapes into categories. Have your child color all the flat shapes in the top row and all the solid shapes in the middle row.
Then have your child color all the triangles in the bottom row.

260 Lesson 30 Name Shapes

©Curriculum Associates, LLC   Copying is not permitted.

You may wish to assign the following pages for practice after completing the first Guided Practice in *Ready Mathematics.*

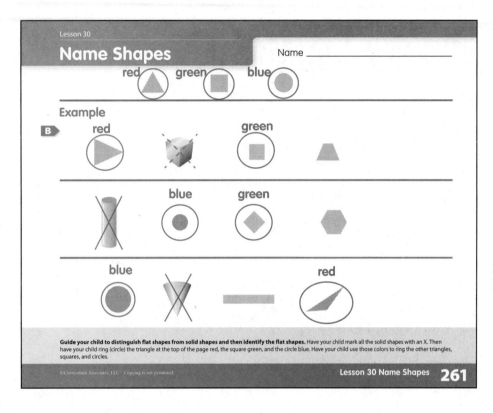

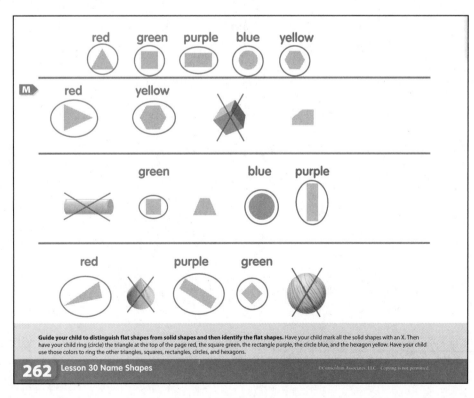

You may wish to assign the following pages for practice after completing the second Guided Practice in **Ready Mathematics.**

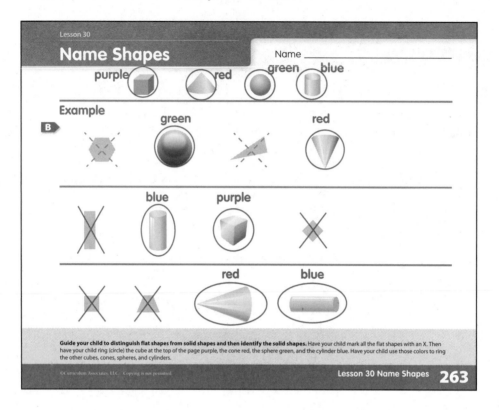

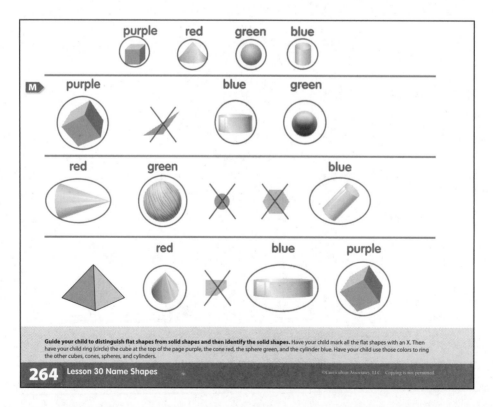

You may wish to assign the following pages for practice after completing the Modeled Instruction in *Ready Mathematics.*

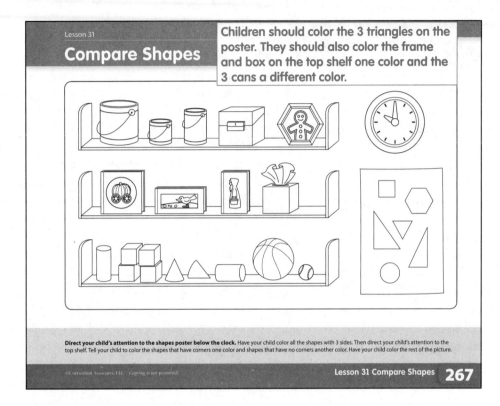

Lesson 31

Compare Shapes

Children should color the 3 triangles on the poster. They should also color the frame and box on the top shelf one color and the 3 cans a different color.

Direct your child's attention to the shapes poster below the clock. Have your child color all the shapes with 3 sides. Then direct your child's attention to the top shelf. Tell your child to color the shapes that have corners one color and shapes that have no corners another color. Have your child color the rest of the picture.

©Curriculum Associates, LLC   Copying is not permitted.

Lesson 31 Compare Shapes **267**

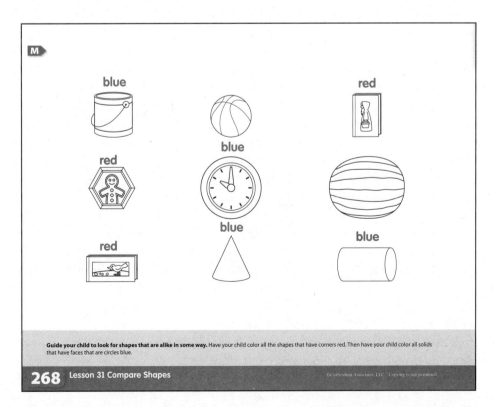

M

blue

red

red

blue

red

blue

blue

blue

red

Guide your child to look for shapes that are alike in some way. Have your child color all the shapes that have corners red. Then have your child color all solids that have faces that are circles blue.

268 Lesson 31 Compare Shapes

©Curriculum Associates, LLC   Copying is not permitted.

You may wish to assign the following pages for practice after completing the first Guided Practice in *Ready Mathematics.*

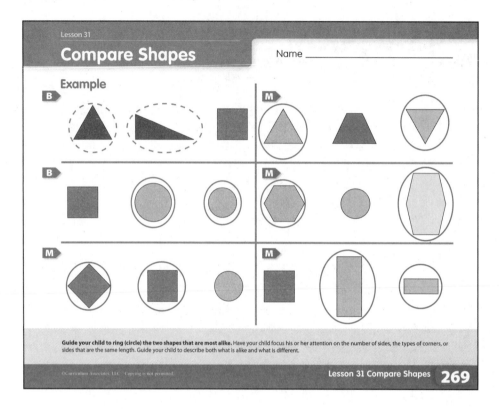

Lesson 31

Compare Shapes

Name _____

Example

Guide your child to ring (circle) the two shapes that are most alike. Have your child focus his or her attention on the number of sides, the types of corners, or sides that are the same length. Guide your child to describe both what is alike and what is different.

©Curriculum Associates, LLC Copying is not permitted.

Lesson 31 Compare Shapes **269**

Key

B Basic

M Medium

C Challenge

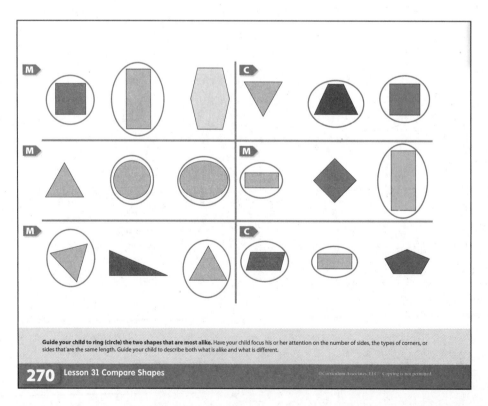

Guide your child to ring (circle) the two shapes that are most alike. Have your child focus his or her attention on the number of sides, the types of corners, or sides that are the same length. Guide your child to describe both what is alike and what is different.

270 Lesson 31 Compare Shapes

©Curriculum Associates, LLC Copying is not permitted.

You may wish to assign the following pages for practice after completing the second Guided Practice in *Ready Mathematics*.

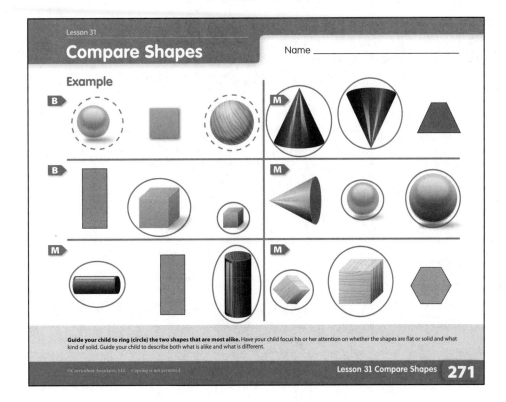

Guide your child to ring (circle) the two shapes that are most alike. Have your child focus his or her attention on whether the shapes are flat or solid and what kind of solid. Guide your child to describe both what is alike and what is different.

©Curriculum Associates, LLC   Copying is not permitted.

Lesson 31 Compare Shapes **271**

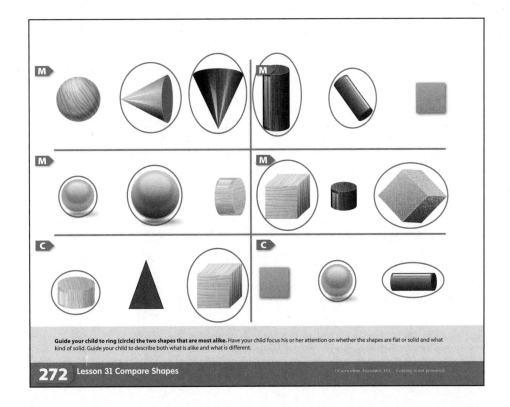

Guide your child to ring (circle) the two shapes that are most alike. Have your child focus his or her attention on whether the shapes are flat or solid and what kind of solid. Guide your child to describe both what is alike and what is different.

272 Lesson 31 Compare Shapes

©Curriculum Associates, LLC   Copying is not permitted.

You may wish to assign the following pages for practice after completing the Modeled Instruction in *Ready Mathematics*.

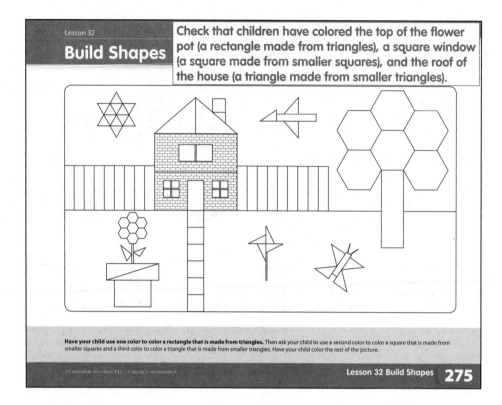

Lesson 32

Build Shapes

Check that children have colored the top of the flower pot (a rectangle made from triangles), a square window (a square made from smaller squares), and the roof of the house (a triangle made from smaller triangles).

Have your child use one color to color a rectangle that is made from triangles. Then ask your child to use a second color to color a square that is made from smaller squares and a third color to color a triangle that is made from smaller triangles. Have your child color the rest of the picture.

©Curriculum Associates, LLC   Copying is not permitted.   **Lesson 32 Build Shapes** **275**

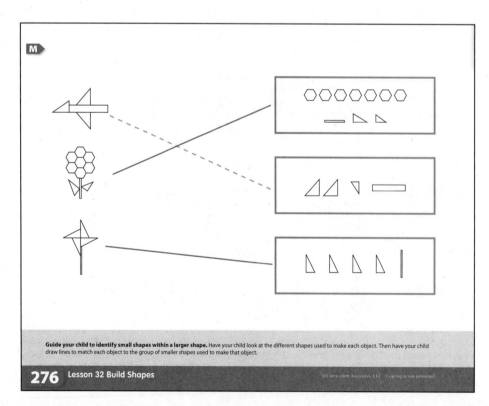

M

Guide your child to identify small shapes within a larger shape. Have your child look at the different shapes used to make each object. Then have your child draw lines to match each object to the group of smaller shapes used to make that object.

276 Lesson 32 Build Shapes   ©Curriculum Associates, LLC   Copying is not permitted.

You may wish to assign the following pages for practice after completing the first Guided Practice in *Ready Mathematics*.

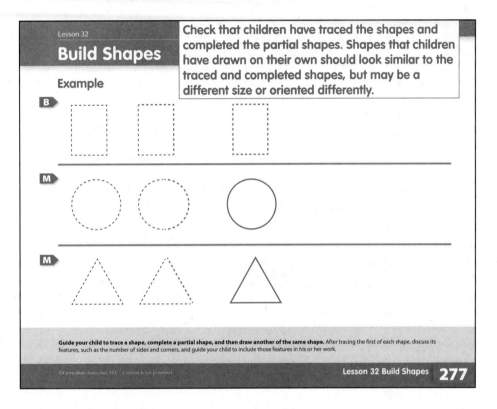

Lesson 32

Build Shapes

Example

Check that children have traced the shapes and completed the partial shapes. Shapes that children have drawn on their own should look similar to the traced and completed shapes, but may be a different size or oriented differently.

Guide your child to trace a shape, complete a partial shape, and then draw another of the same shape. After tracing the first of each shape, discuss its features, such as the number of sides and corners, and guide your child to include those features in his or her work.

©Curriculum Associates, LLC   Copying is not permitted.

Lesson 32 Build Shapes **277**

Key

B Basic

M Medium

C Challenge

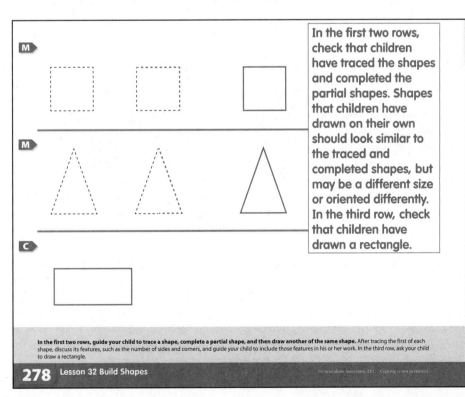

In the first two rows, check that children have traced the shapes and completed the partial shapes. Shapes that children have drawn on their own should look similar to the traced and completed shapes, but may be a different size or oriented differently. In the third row, check that children have drawn a rectangle.

In the first two rows, guide your child to trace a shape, complete a partial shape, and then draw another of the same shape. After tracing the first of each shape, discuss its features, such as the number of sides and corners, and guide your child to include those features in his or her work. In the third row, ask your child to draw a rectangle.

278 Lesson 32 Build Shapes

©Curriculum Associates, LLC   Copying is not permitted.

You may wish to assign the following pages for practice after completing the second Guided Practice in *Ready Mathematics.*

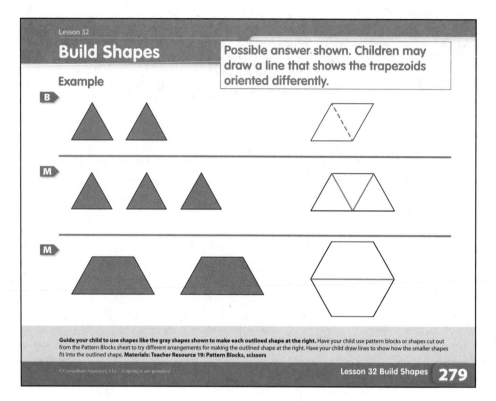

Lesson 32

Build Shapes

Possible answer shown. Children may draw a line that shows the trapezoids oriented differently.

Example

B

M

M

Guide your child to use shapes like the gray shapes shown to make each outlined shape at the right. Have your child use pattern blocks or shapes cut out from the Pattern Blocks sheet to try different arrangements for making the outlined shape at the right. Have your child draw lines to show how the smaller shapes fit into the outlined shape. **Materials: Teacher Resource 19: Pattern Blocks, scissors**

©Curriculum Associates, LLC　Copying is not permitted.　　　　　　　Lesson 32 Build Shapes **279**

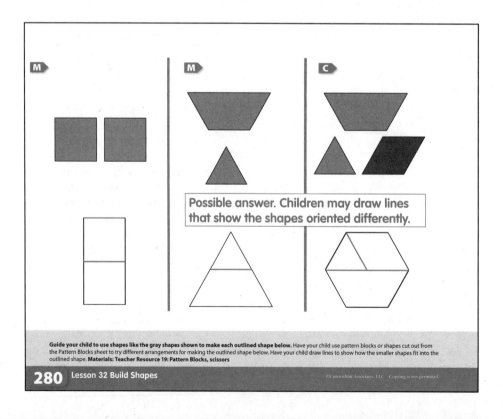

M　　**M**　　**C**

Possible answer. Children may draw lines that show the shapes oriented differently.

Guide your child to use shapes like the gray shapes shown to make each outlined shape below. Have your child use pattern blocks or shapes cut out from the Pattern Blocks sheet to try different arrangements for making the outlined shape below. Have your child draw lines to show how the smaller shapes fit into the outlined shape. **Materials: Teacher Resource 19: Pattern Blocks, scissors**

280 Lesson 32 Build Shapes　　　　　　　　©Curriculum Associates, LLC　Copying is not permitted.

Unit 7 Practice
Shapes

Name _____

M   3 sides   **M**   ◯ face

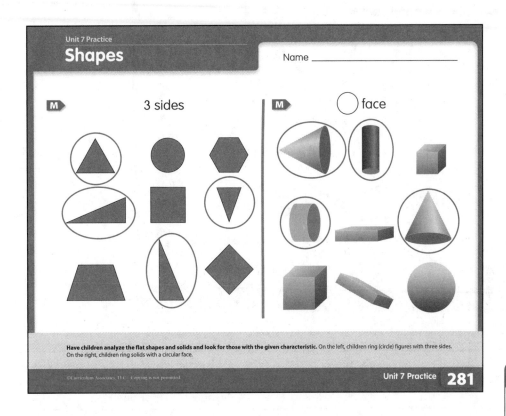

Have children analyze the flat shapes and solids and look for those with the given characteristic. On the left, children ring (circle) figures with three sides.
On the right, children ring solids with a circular face.

©Curriculum Associates, LLC   Copying is not permitted.

Unit 7 Practice **281**

Pictures will vary. Children's pictures should include some combination of triangles and squares.

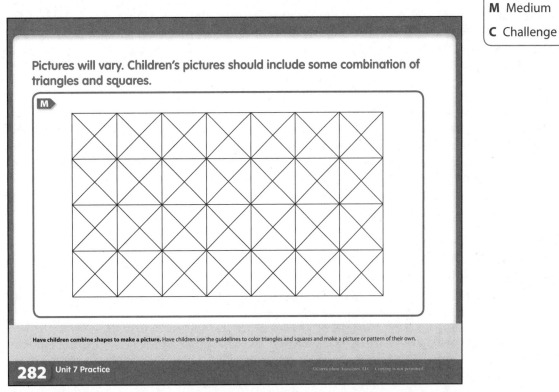

Have children combine shapes to make a picture. Have children use the guidelines to color triangles and squares and make a picture or pattern of their own.

282 Unit 7 Practice   ©Curriculum Associates, LLC   Copying is not permitted.

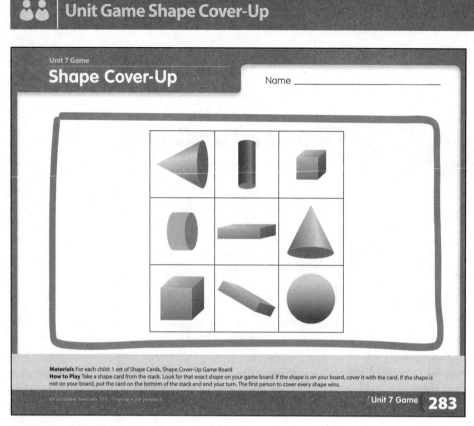

Unit 7 Game

Shape Cover-Up

Name _____

Materials For each child: 1 set of Shape Cards, Shape Cover-Up Game Board
How to Play Take a shape card from the stack. Look for that exact shape on your game board. If the shape is on your board, cover it with the card. If the shape is not on your board, put the card on the bottom of the stack and end your turn. The first person to cover every shape wins.

©Curriculum Associates, LLC Copying is not permitted.　　　Unit 7 Game **283**

STEP BY STEP

CCSS Focus - K.G.A.3, K.G.B.4 *Embedded SMPs* - 1, 4, 7 **Objective:** Match pictures of flat and solid shapes.	**Materials:** For each child: game board, Shape Cards (Teacher Resource 16), Shape Cover-Up Recording Sheet (Teacher Resource 18) (optional)

- **Take a shape card from the stack. Look for that exact shape on your game board. If the shape is on your board, cover it with the card.** Read the first three sentences of the *How to Play* aloud. After each step, ask children to explain in their own words what to do.

- **If the shape is not on your board, put the card on the bottom of the stack and end your turn. The first person to cover every shape wins.** Finish reading *How to Play*, making sure children understand the rules and how to complete the game. Children play in pairs, but each player gets his/her own game board and set of 12 shape cards.

- Model pulling a card and think aloud as you figure out which shape on the game board it matches. Encourage children to share their thinking as well.

- During the game, circulate and encourage children to name and describe the shapes as they play.

- After children have played a game, they may use the optional recording sheet to sort the shape cards as flat or solid, count the cards in each box, and write the total.

Vary the Game Have children use Real-World Shape Cards (Teacher Resource 17) instead of the Shape Cards. Pairs place each card on the square with the matching shape on their own game boards. The player who matches all cards fastest wins.

Extra Support To support children who may find it difficult to visualize solid shapes, have them play using only the flat shapes. Make an extra copy of the shape cards so each child has more cards to draw from.

Fluency Practice
Table of Contents

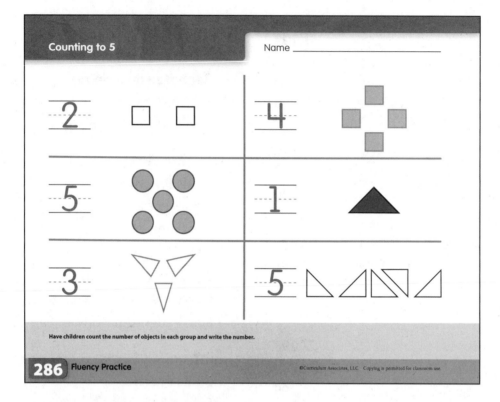

Counting to 5

Name _____

2

4

5

1

3

5

Have children count the number of objects in each group and write the number.

©Curriculum Associates, LLC   Copying is permitted for classroom use.

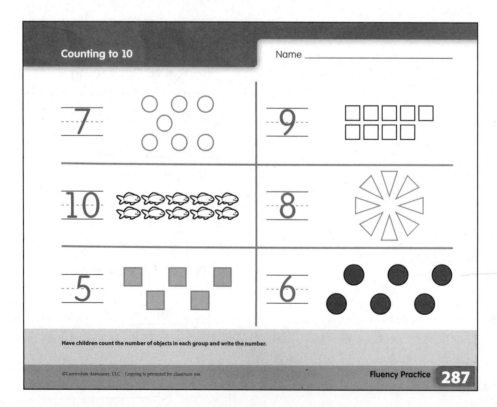

Counting to 10

Name _____

7

9

10

8

5

6

Have children count the number of objects in each group and write the number.

©Curriculum Associates, LLC   Copying is permitted for classroom use.

Counting to 20

Name _____

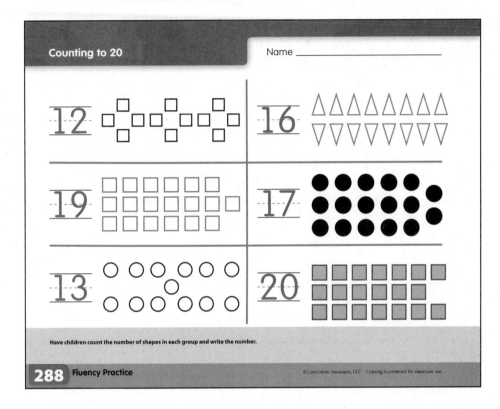

12

16

19

17

13

20

Have children count the number of shapes in each group and write the number.

©Curriculum Associates, LLC   Copying is permitted for classroom use.

Counting to 50

Name _____

24	25	**26**	**40**	41	42
43	**44**	45	33	34	**35**
37	38	39	29	**30**	31
27	**28**	29	48	49	**50**

Guide children to count and find the missing number. Have children write the missing number in each list.

©Curriculum Associates, LLC   Copying is permitted for classroom use.

Counting to 100

Name _____

52	53	**54**	79	**80**	81
76	**77**	78	**63**	64	65
69	70	71	98	99	**100**
87	88	**89**	58	**59**	60

Guide children to count and find the missing number. Have children write the missing number in each list.

©Curriculum Associates, LLC   Copying is permitted for classroom use.

Find Patterns in Counting by Tens—Repeated Reasoning

Name _____

1	2	3	4	5	6	7	8	9	10
11	12	13	14	15	16	17	18	19	☐
21	22	23	24	25	26	27	28	29	30
31	32	33	34	35	36	37	38	39	40
41	42	43	44	45	46	47	48	49	☐
51	52	53	54	55	56	57	58	59	60
61	62	63	64	65	66	67	68	69	☐
71	72	73	74	75	76	77	78	79	80
81	82	83	84	85	86	87	88	89	90
91	92	93	94	95	96	97	98	99	☐

20

50

70

100

Guide children to point to the numbers in the far right column of the chart as they count by tens to 100. When they get to a blank box, have children write the missing number on the lines next to that box.

Talk About It Look at the numbers in the top row of the chart. Then look at the numbers in the far right column. How is counting by tens like counting by ones?

©Curriculum Associates, LLC   Copying is permitted for classroom use.

Fluency Practice

Find Patterns in Counting by Ones—Repeated Reasoning

Name _____

1	2	3	4	5	6	7	8	9	10
11	12	13	14	15	16	☐	18	19	20
21	22	23	24	25	26	27	28	29	30
31	32	33	☐	35	36	37	38	39	40
41	42	43	44	45	46	47	48	49	50
51	52	53	54	55	56	57	58	☐	60
61	62	63	64	65	66	67	68	69	70
71	72	73	74	75	76	77	78	79	80
☐	82	83	84	85	86	87	88	89	90
91	92	93	94	95	96	97	98	99	100

17

34

59

81

Guide children to point to the numbers on the chart as they count by ones to 100. When they get to a blank box, have children write the missing number on the lines next to that row.

Talk About It How are the numbers in each row alike? How are the numbers in each column alike? What patterns do you see in the numbers as you count to 100?

292 Fluency Practice

©Curriculum Associates, LLC Copying is permitted for classroom use.

Number Pairs to 3

Name _____

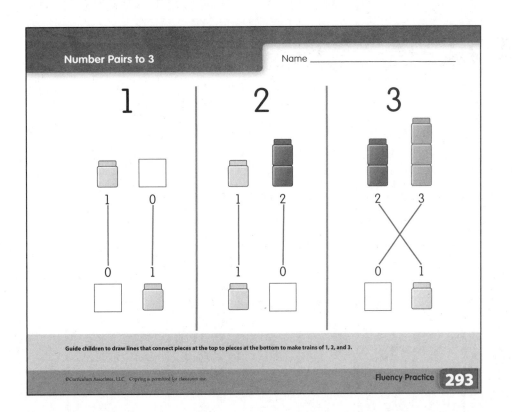

Guide children to draw lines that connect pieces at the top to pieces at the bottom to make trains of 1, 2, and 3.

©Curriculum Associates, LLC Copying is permitted for classroom use.

Fluency Practice **293**

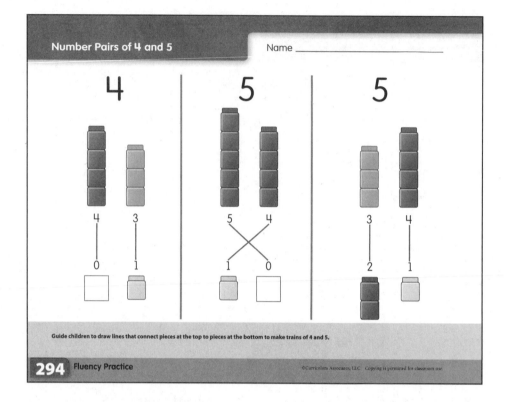

Guide children to draw lines that connect pieces at the top to pieces at the bottom to make trains of 4 and 5.

©Curriculum Associates, LLC   Copying is permitted for classroom use.

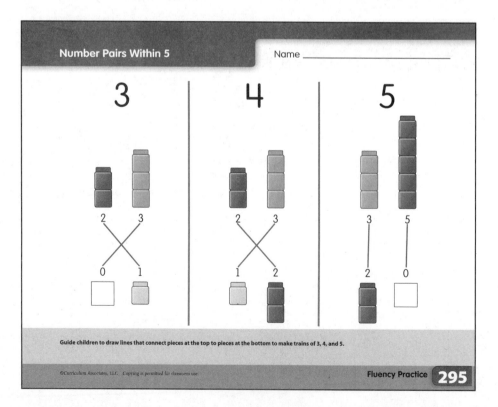

Guide children to draw lines that connect pieces at the top to pieces at the bottom to make trains of 3, 4, and 5.

©Curriculum Associates, LLC   Copying is permitted for classroom use.

©Curriculum Associates, LLC   Copying is not permitted.

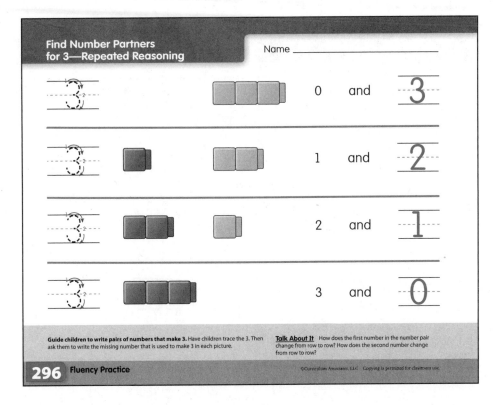

Find Number Partners
for 3—Repeated Reasoning

Name _____

Guide children to write pairs of numbers that make 3. Have children trace the 3. Then ask them to write the missing number that is used to make 3 in each picture.

Talk About It How does the first number in the number pair change from row to row? How does the second number change from row to row?

296 Fluency Practice

©Curriculum Associates, LLC   Copying is permitted for classroom use.

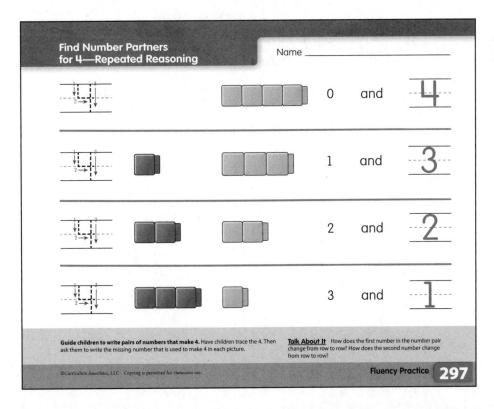

Find Number Partners
for 4—Repeated Reasoning

Name _____

Guide children to write pairs of numbers that make 4. Have children trace the 4. Then ask them to write the missing number that is used to make 4 in each picture.

Talk About It How does the first number in the number pair change from row to row? How does the second number change from row to row?

©Curriculum Associates, LLC   Copying is permitted for classroom use.

Fluency Practice **297**

Find Sums to 3

Name _____

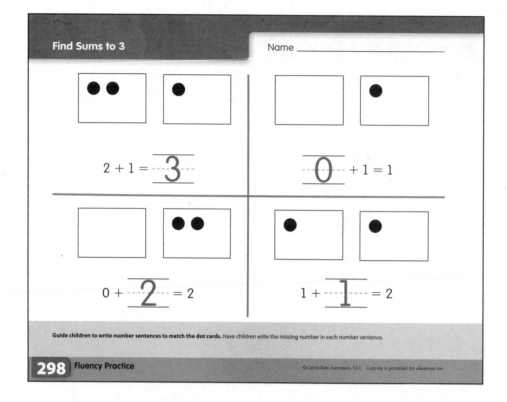

$2 + 1 = 3$

$0 + 1 = 1$

$0 + 2 = 2$

$1 + 1 = 2$

Guide children to write number sentences to match the dot cards. Have children write the missing number in each number sentence.

Find Sums of 4 and 5

Name _____

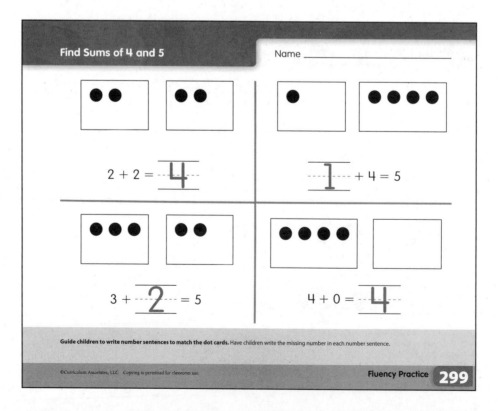

$2 + 2 = 4$

$1 + 4 = 5$

$3 + 2 = 5$

$4 + 0 = 4$

Guide children to write number sentences to match the dot cards. Have children write the missing number in each number sentence.

Find Sums Within 5

Name _____

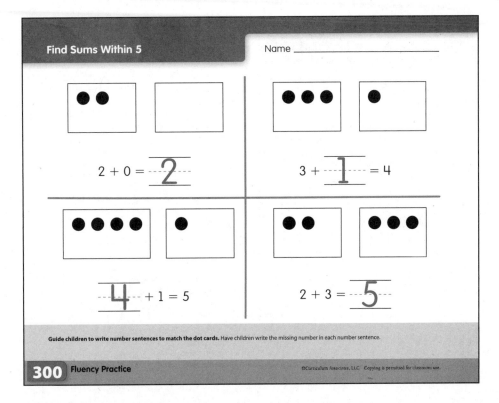

$2 + 0 = 2$

$3 + 1 = 4$

$4 + 1 = 5$

$2 + 3 = 5$

Guide children to write number sentences to match the dot cards. Have children write the missing number in each number sentence.

Find Patterns When Adding 1—Repeated Reasoning

Name _____

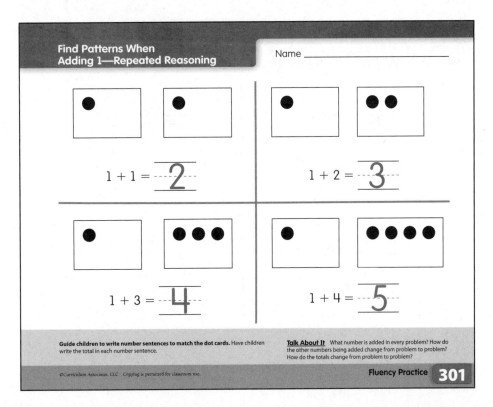

$1 + 1 = 2$

$1 + 2 = 3$

$1 + 3 = 4$

$1 + 4 = 5$

Guide children to write number sentences to match the dot cards. Have children write the total in each number sentence.

Talk About It What number is added in every problem? How do the other numbers being added change from problem to problem? How do the totals change from problem to problem?

Find Patterns When Adding 0—Repeated Reasoning

Name _____

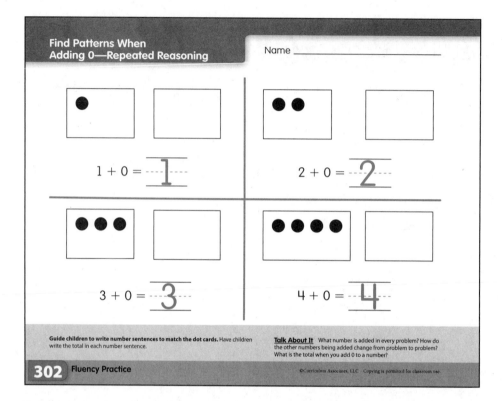

$1 + 0 = \underline{1}$

$2 + 0 = \underline{2}$

$3 + 0 = \underline{3}$

$4 + 0 = \underline{4}$

Guide children to write number sentences to match the dot cards. Have children write the total in each number sentence.

Talk About It What number is added in every problem? How do the other numbers being added change from problem to problem? What is the total when you add 0 to a number?

302 Fluency Practice

©Curriculum Associates, LLC · Copying is permitted for classroom use.

Subtract Within 3

Name _____

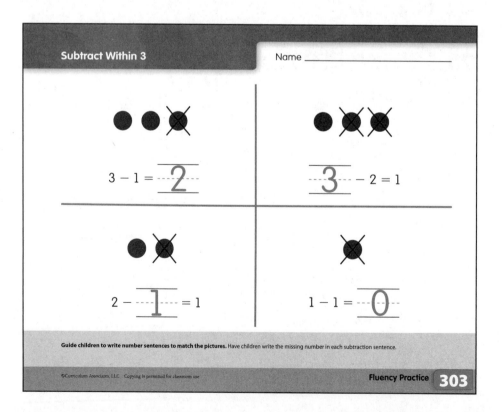

$3 - 1 = \underline{2}$

$\underline{3} - 2 = 1$

$2 - \underline{1} = 1$

$1 - 1 = \underline{0}$

Guide children to write number sentences to match the pictures. Have children write the missing number in each subtraction sentence.

©Curriculum Associates, LLC Copying is permitted for classroom use

Fluency Practice **303**

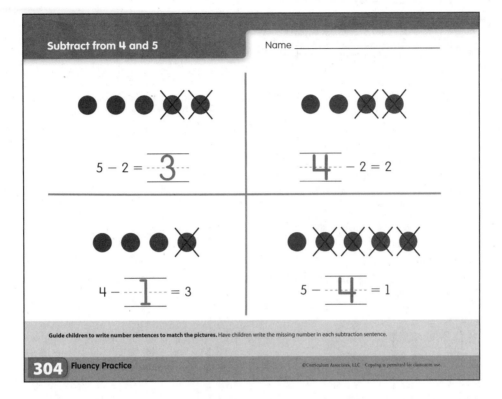

Subtract from 4 and 5

Name _____

$5 - 2 = 3$

$4 - 2 = 2$

$4 - 1 = 3$

$5 - 4 = 1$

Guide children to write number sentences to match the pictures. Have children write the missing number in each subtraction sentence.

304 Fluency Practice

©Curriculum Associates, LLC Copying is permitted for classroom use.

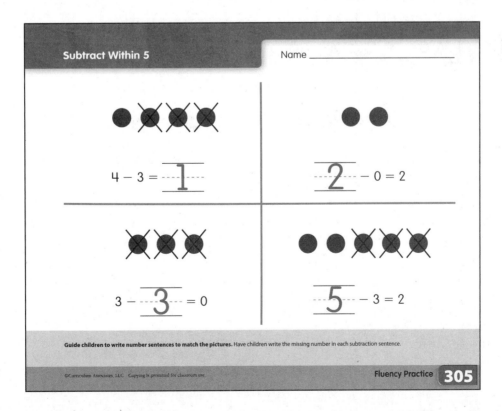

Subtract Within 5

Name _____

$4 - 3 = 1$

$2 - 0 = 2$

$3 - 3 = 0$

$5 - 3 = 2$

Guide children to write number sentences to match the pictures. Have children write the missing number in each subtraction sentence.

©Curriculum Associates, LLC Copying is permitted for classroom use.

Fluency Practice **305**

Find Patterns with Differences of 1—Repeated Reasoning

Name _____

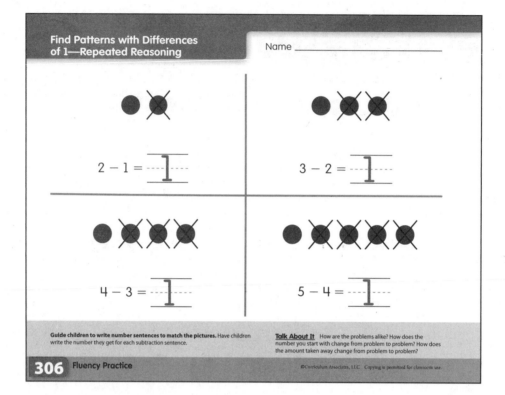

$2 - 1 = \underline{1}$

$3 - 2 = \underline{1}$

$4 - 3 = \underline{1}$

$5 - 4 = \underline{1}$

Guide children to write number sentences to match the pictures. Have children write the number they get for each subtraction sentence.

Talk About It How are the problems alike? How does the number you start with change from problem to problem? How does the amount taken away change from problem to problem?

306 Fluency Practice

©Curriculum Associates, LLC   Copying is permitted for classroom use.

Find Patterns When Subtracting from 4—Repeated Reasoning

Name _____

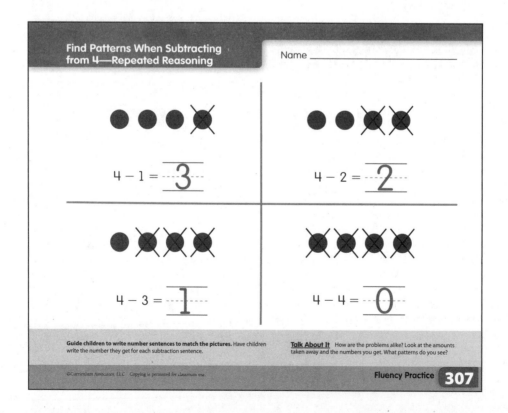

$4 - 1 = \underline{3}$

$4 - 2 = \underline{2}$

$4 - 3 = \underline{1}$

$4 - 4 = \underline{0}$

Guide children to write number sentences to match the pictures. Have children write the number they get for each subtraction sentence.

Talk About It How are the problems alike? Look at the amounts taken away and the numbers you get. What patterns do you see?

©Curriculum Associates, LLC   Copying is permitted for classroom use.

Fluency Practice **307**

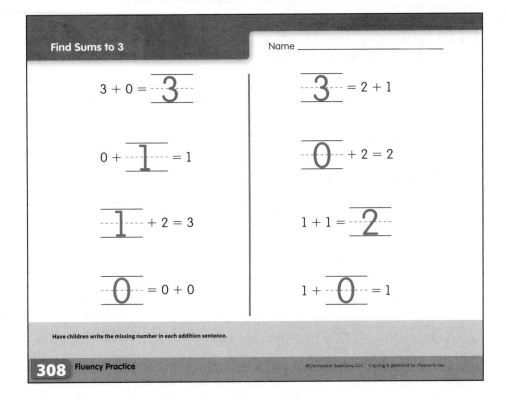

Find Sums to 3

Name _____

$3 + 0 = \underline{3}$

$\underline{3} = 2 + 1$

$0 + \underline{1} = 1$

$\underline{0} + 2 = 2$

$\underline{1} + 2 = 3$

$1 + 1 = \underline{2}$

$\underline{0} = 0 + 0$

$1 + \underline{0} = 1$

Have children write the missing number in each addition sentence.

308 **Fluency Practice**

©Curriculum Associates, LLC   Copying is permitted for classroom use.

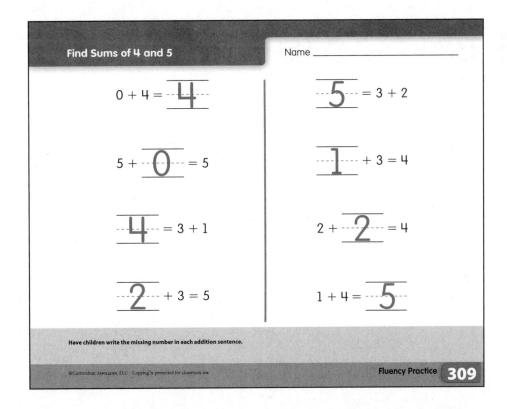

Find Sums of 4 and 5

Name _____

$0 + 4 = \underline{4}$

$\underline{5} = 3 + 2$

$5 + \underline{0} = 5$

$\underline{1} + 3 = 4$

$\underline{4} = 3 + 1$

$2 + \underline{2} = 4$

$\underline{2} + 3 = 5$

$1 + 4 = \underline{5}$

Have children write the missing number in each addition sentence.

©Curriculum Associates, LLC   Copying is permitted for classroom use.

Fluency Practice **309**

Find Sums Within 5

Name _____

$2 + 0 = \underline{2}$

$2 + \underline{1} = 3$

$\underline{4} = 2 + 2$

$\underline{0} + 5 = 5$

$\underline{5} = 4 + 1$

$\underline{1} + 1 = 2$

$0 + \underline{3} = 3$

$1 + 3 = \underline{4}$

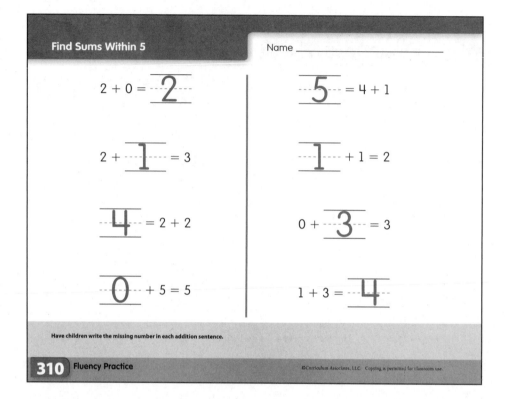

Have children write the missing number in each addition sentence.

©Curriculum Associates, LLC   Copying is permitted for classroom use.

Find Patterns with Sums to 5—Repeated Reasoning

Name _____

$2 + 0 = \underline{2}$

$2 + 1 = \underline{3}$

$2 + 2 = \underline{4}$

$2 + 3 = \underline{5}$

$3 + 0 = \underline{3}$

$3 + 1 = \underline{4}$

$3 + 2 = \underline{5}$

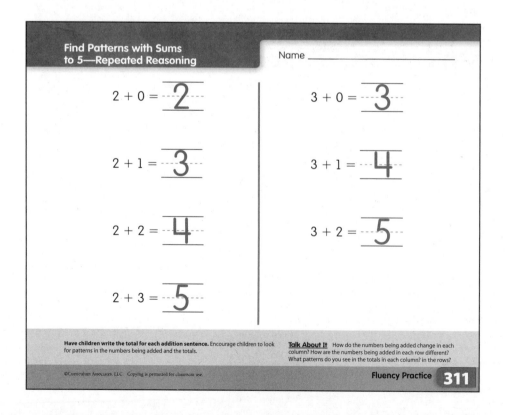

Have children write the total for each addition sentence. Encourage children to look for patterns in the numbers being added and the totals.

Talk About It How do the numbers being added change in each column? How are the numbers being added in each row different? What patterns do you see in the totals in each column? in the rows?

©Curriculum Associates, LLC   Copying is permitted for classroom use.

Fluency Practice

Find Patterns in Number Partners—Repeated Reasoning

Name _____

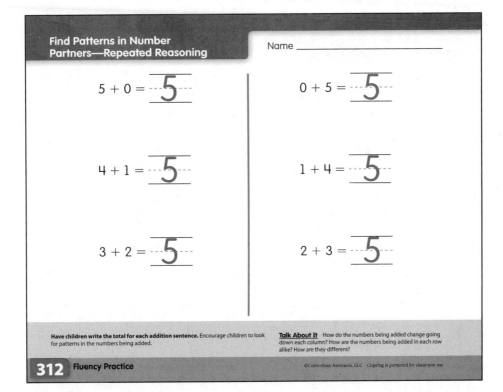

$5 + 0 =$ **5**

$0 + 5 =$ **5**

$4 + 1 =$ **5**

$1 + 4 =$ **5**

$3 + 2 =$ **5**

$2 + 3 =$ **5**

Have children write the total for each addition sentence. Encourage children to look for patterns in the numbers being added.

Talk About It How do the numbers being added change going down each column? How are the numbers being added in each row alike? How are they different?

312 Fluency Practice

©Curriculum Associates, LLC   Copying is permitted for classroom use.

Subtract Within 3

Name _____

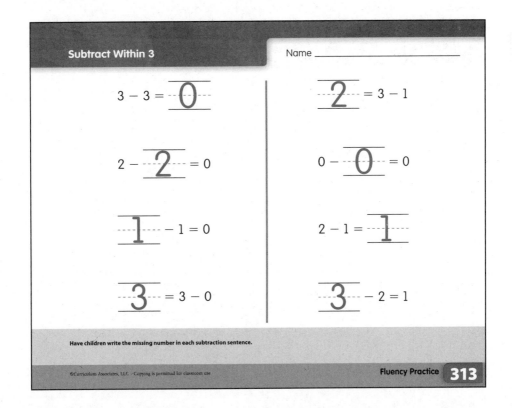

$3 - 3 =$ **0**

2 $= 3 - 1$

$2 -$ **2** $= 0$

$0 -$ **0** $= 0$

1 $- 1 = 0$

$2 - 1 =$ **1**

3 $= 3 - 0$

3 $- 2 = 1$

Have children write the missing number in each subtraction sentence.

©Curriculum Associates, LLC   Copying is permitted for classroom use.

Fluency Practice **313**

Subtract from 4 and 5

Name _____

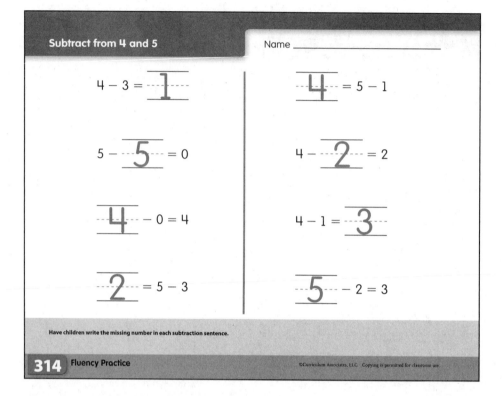

$4 - 3 = \boxed{1}$

$\boxed{4} = 5 - 1$

$5 - \boxed{5} = 0$

$4 - \boxed{2} = 2$

$\boxed{4} - 0 = 4$

$4 - 1 = \boxed{3}$

$\boxed{2} = 5 - 3$

$\boxed{5} - 2 = 3$

Have children write the missing number in each subtraction sentence.

314 Fluency Practice

Subtract Within 5

Name _____

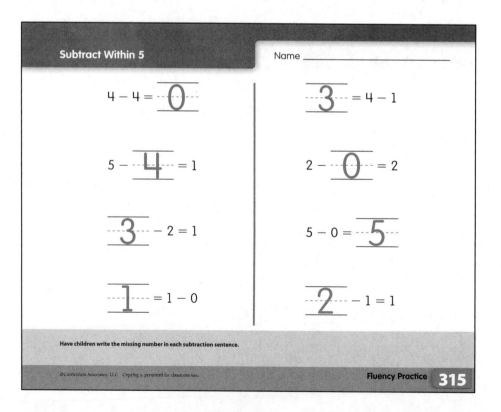

$4 - 4 = \boxed{0}$

$\boxed{3} = 4 - 1$

$5 - \boxed{4} = 1$

$2 - \boxed{0} = 2$

$\boxed{3} - 2 = 1$

$5 - 0 = \boxed{5}$

$\boxed{1} = 1 - 0$

$\boxed{2} - 1 = 1$

Have children write the missing number in each subtraction sentence.

Fluency Practice **315**

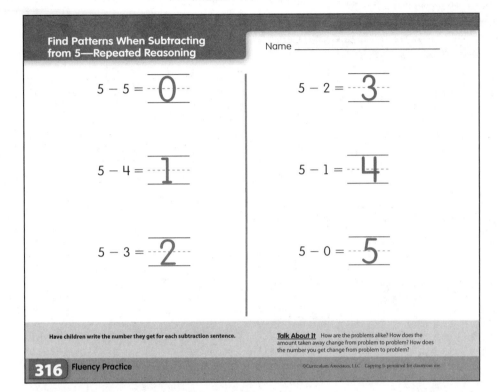

Find Patterns When Subtracting from 5—Repeated Reasoning

Name _____

$5 - 5 = 0$

$5 - 4 = 1$

$5 - 3 = 2$

$5 - 2 = 3$

$5 - 1 = 4$

$5 - 0 = 5$

Have children write the number they get for each subtraction sentence.

Talk About It How are the problems alike? How does the amount taken away change from problem to problem? How does the number you get change from problem to problem?

316 Fluency Practice

©Curriculum Associates, LLC   Copying is permitted for classroom use.

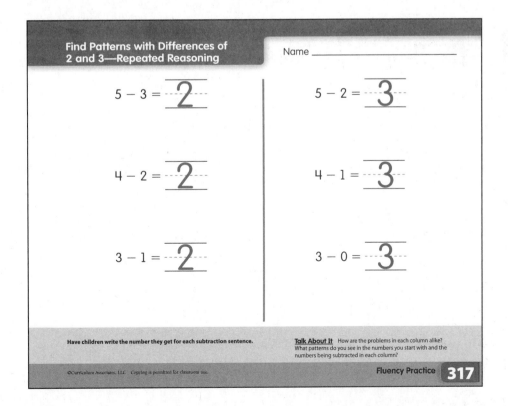

Find Patterns with Differences of 2 and 3—Repeated Reasoning

Name _____

$5 - 3 = 2$

$4 - 2 = 2$

$3 - 1 = 2$

$5 - 2 = 3$

$4 - 1 = 3$

$3 - 0 = 3$

Have children write the number they get for each subtraction sentence.

Talk About It How are the problems in each column alike? What patterns do you see in the numbers you start with and the numbers being subtracted in each column?

©Curriculum Associates, LLC   Copying is permitted for classroom use.

Fluency Practice **317**

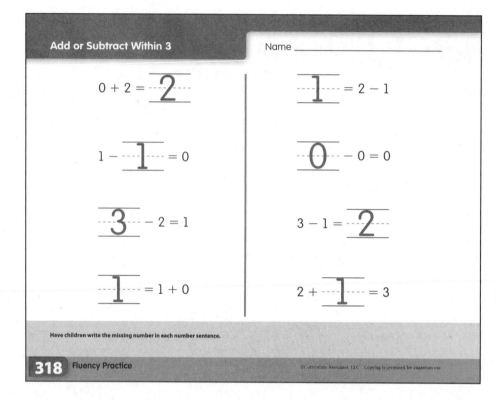

Add or Subtract Within 3

Name _____

$0 + 2 = \underline{2}$

$\underline{1} = 2 - 1$

$1 - \underline{1} = 0$

$\underline{0} - 0 = 0$

$\underline{3} - 2 = 1$

$3 - 1 = \underline{2}$

$\underline{1} = 1 + 0$

$2 + \underline{1} = 3$

Have children write the missing number in each number sentence.

©Curriculum Associates, LLC   Copying is permitted for classroom use.

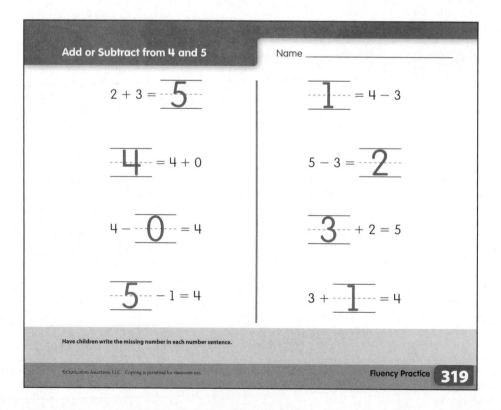

Add or Subtract from 4 and 5

Name _____

$2 + 3 = \underline{5}$

$\underline{1} = 4 - 3$

$\underline{4} = 4 + 0$

$5 - 3 = \underline{2}$

$4 - \underline{0} = 4$

$\underline{3} + 2 = 5$

$\underline{5} - 1 = 4$

$3 + \underline{1} = 4$

Have children write the missing number in each number sentence.

©Curriculum Associates, LLC   Copying is permitted for classroom use.

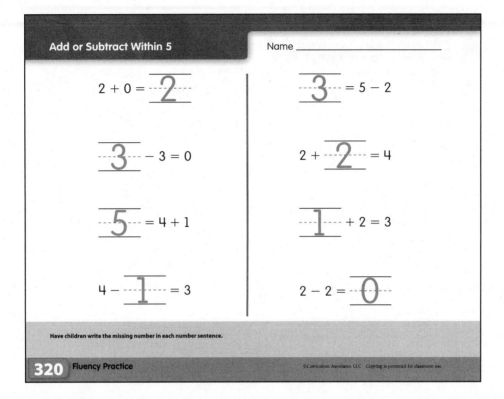

Add or Subtract Within 5

Name _____

$2 + 0 = \underline{2}$

$\underline{3} = 5 - 2$

$\underline{3} - 3 = 0$

$2 + \underline{2} = 4$

$\underline{5} = 4 + 1$

$\underline{1} + 2 = 3$

$4 - \underline{1} = 3$

$2 - 2 = \underline{0}$

Have children write the missing number in each number sentence.

320 Fluency Practice

©Curriculum Associates, LLC   Copying is permitted for classroom use

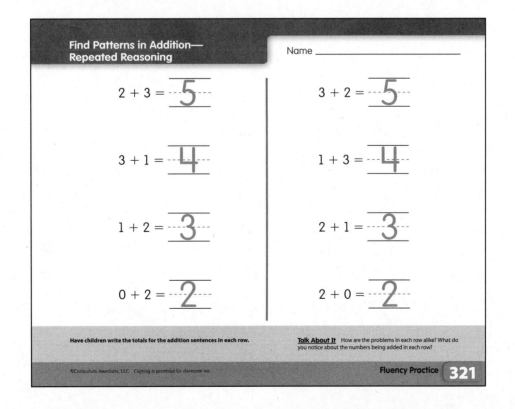

**Find Patterns in Addition—
Repeated Reasoning**

Name _____

$2 + 3 = \underline{5}$

$3 + 2 = \underline{5}$

$3 + 1 = \underline{4}$

$1 + 3 = \underline{4}$

$1 + 2 = \underline{3}$

$2 + 1 = \underline{3}$

$0 + 2 = \underline{2}$

$2 + 0 = \underline{2}$

Have children write the totals for the addition sentences in each row.

Talk About It How are the problems in each row alike? What do you notice about the numbers being added in each row?

©Curriculum Associates, LLC   Copying is permitted for classroom use.

Fluency Practice **321**

Find Patterns in Subtraction—Repeated Reasoning

Name _____

$5 - 5 =$ 0

$5 - 0 =$ 5

$4 - 4 =$ 0

$4 - 0 =$ 4

$3 - 3 =$ 0

$3 - 0 =$ 3

$2 - 2 =$ 0

$2 - 0 =$ 2

Have children write the number they get for each subtraction sentence.

<u>**Talk About It**</u> How are the problems in the left column alike? How are the problems in the right column alike? What patterns do you see?

322 **Fluency Practice**

©Curriculum Associates, LLC   Copying is permitted for classroom use.

Teacher Resource Blackline Masters
Table of Contents

These teacher resources are provided for use with the **Ready® Practice and Problem Solving** lesson practice and games. These teacher resource masters may be phototcopied for classroom use. Teacher Resources 1–18 are for use with unit games. Refer to the unit game support in the **Ready Practice and Problem Solving** Teacher Guide for a full list of materials and instructions. Teacher Resource 19 is for use with Lesson 32.

Name _____

Roll and Count Game Board

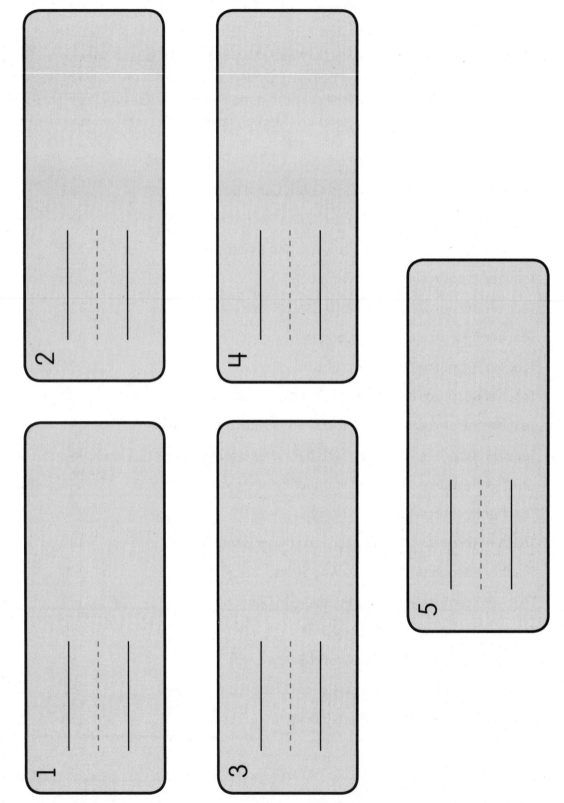

Name _____

Color the Cubes Recording Sheet

Match 6, 7, 8, and 9 Game Board

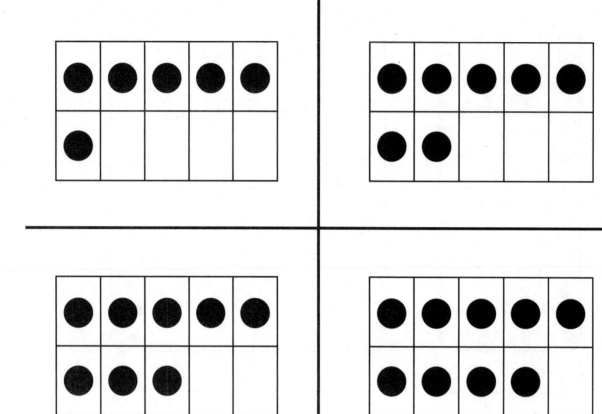

Name _____

Dot Cards
Match 6, 7, 8, and 9 Game Pieces

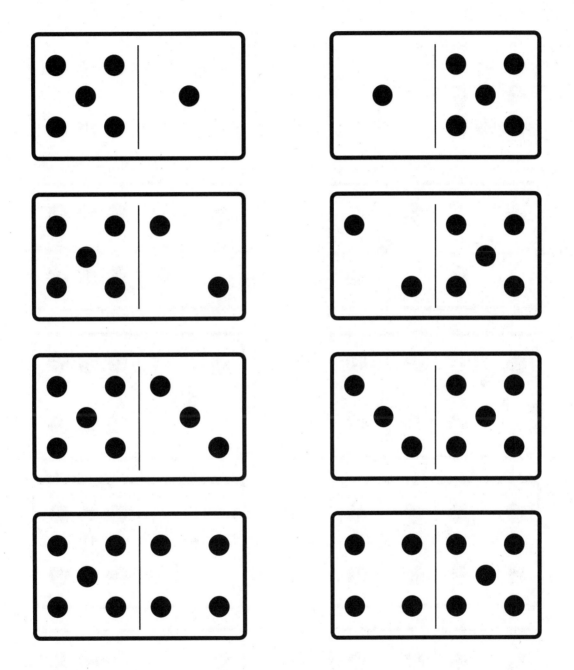

Name _____

Dot Cards
Match 6, 7, 8, and 9 Game Pieces

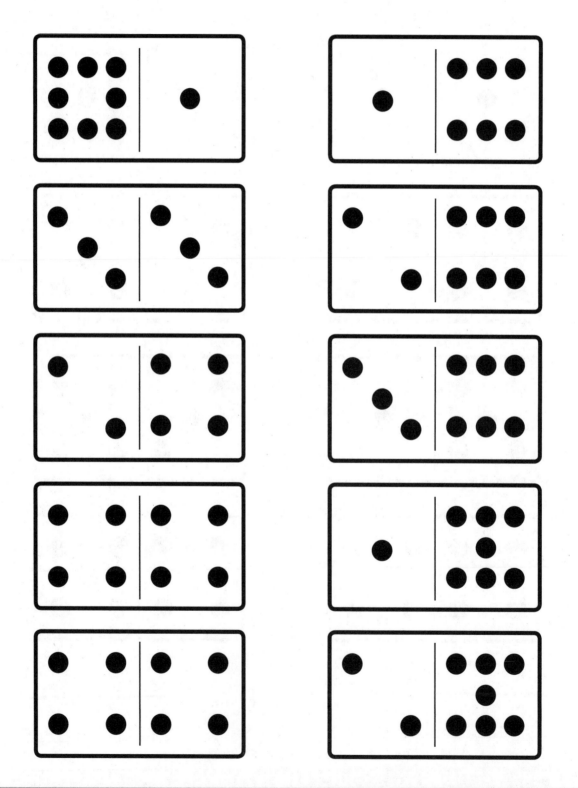

Name _____

Make 10 Game Board

and

and

and

and

Name _____

Dot Cards 1–9

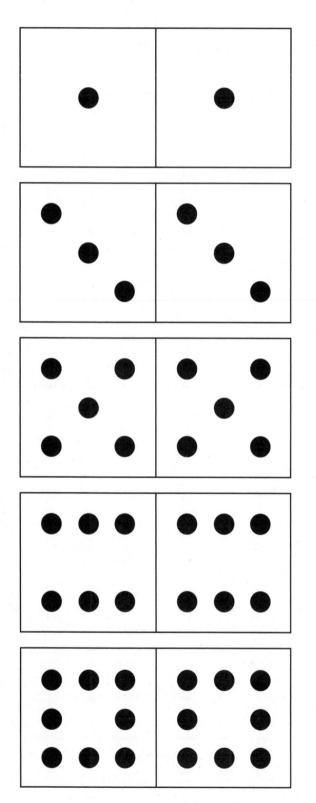
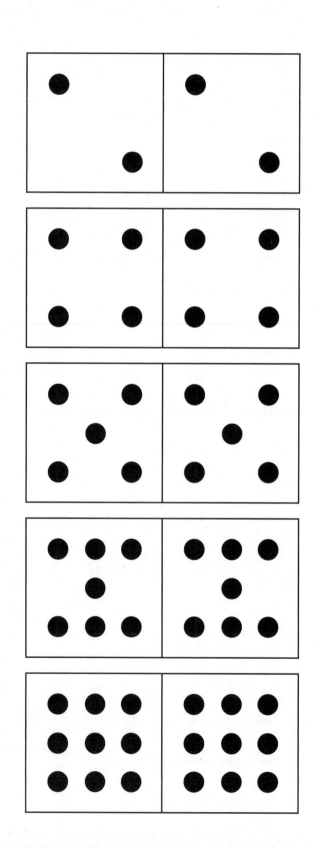

Name _____

Number Cards 1–9

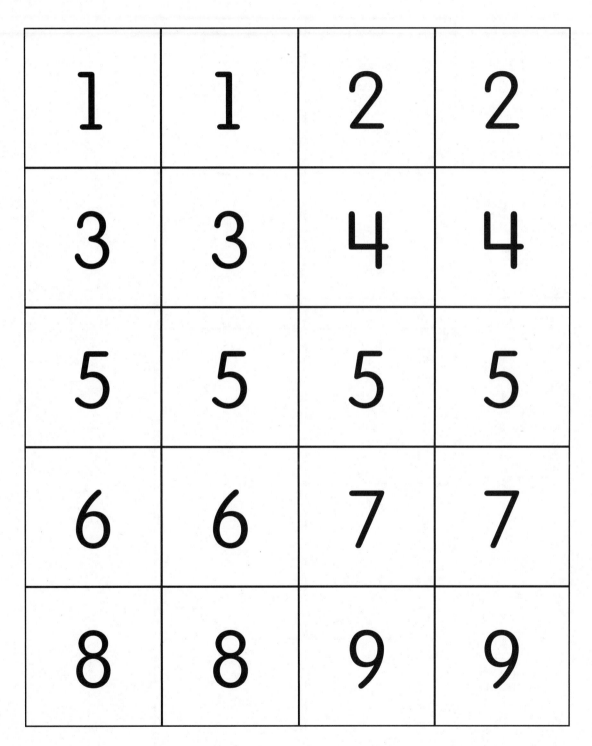

1	1	2	2
3	3	4	4
5	5	5	5
6	6	7	7
8	8	9	9

Last One Wins Game Board

Name _____

Addition Sentence Recording Sheet

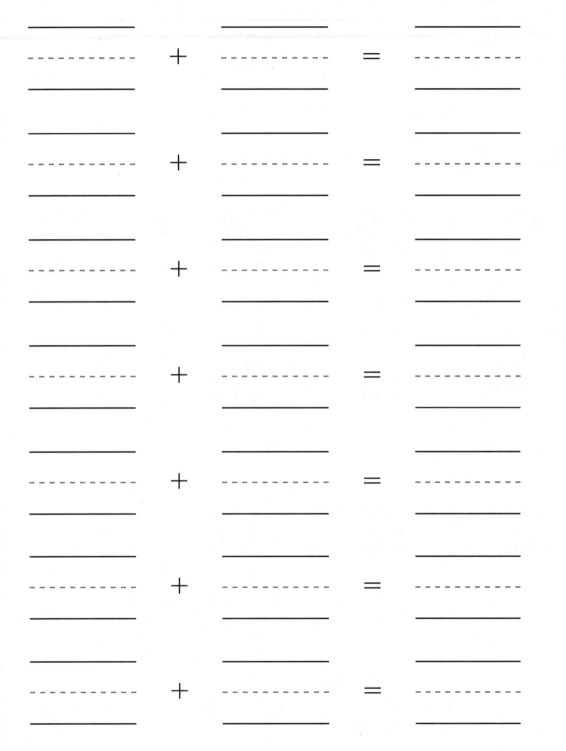

Teen Number Cover-Up Game Board

11	**12**	**13**
14	**15**	**16**
17	**18**	**19**

Name_____

Teen Number Picture Cards

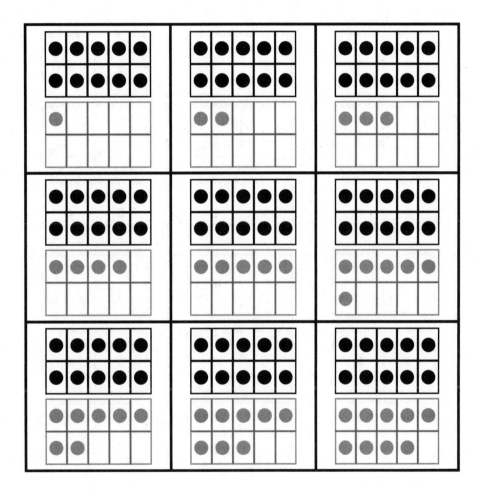

Name _____

TR 11

Teen Number Picture Cards (continued)

Unit Game

Teen Number Picture Cards *(continued)*

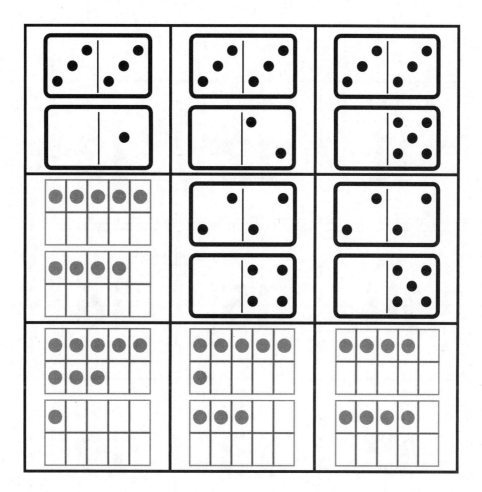

Teen Number Cards

11	**12**	**13**
14	**15**	**16**
17	**18**	**19**

Unit Game

Name _____

Shorter and Longer Game Board

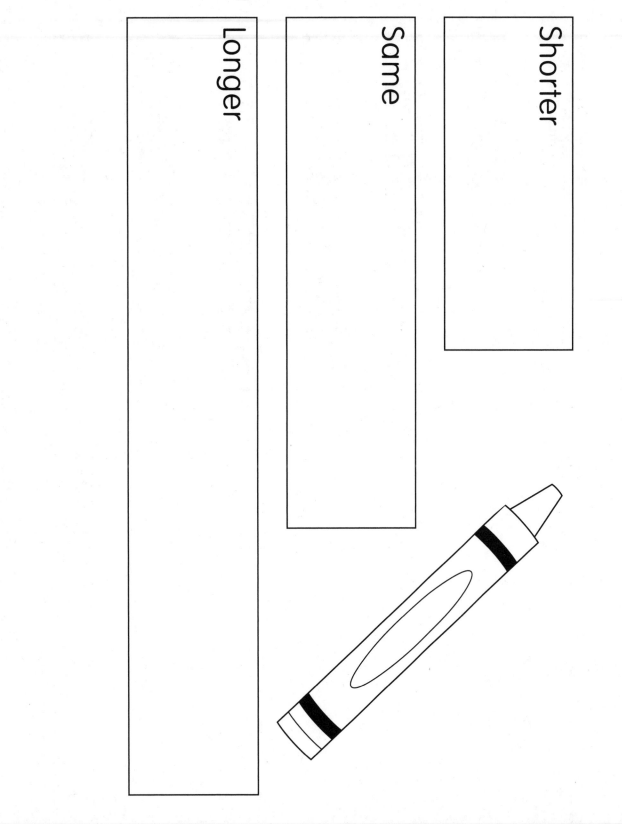

Longer

Same

Shorter

Measuring Strips

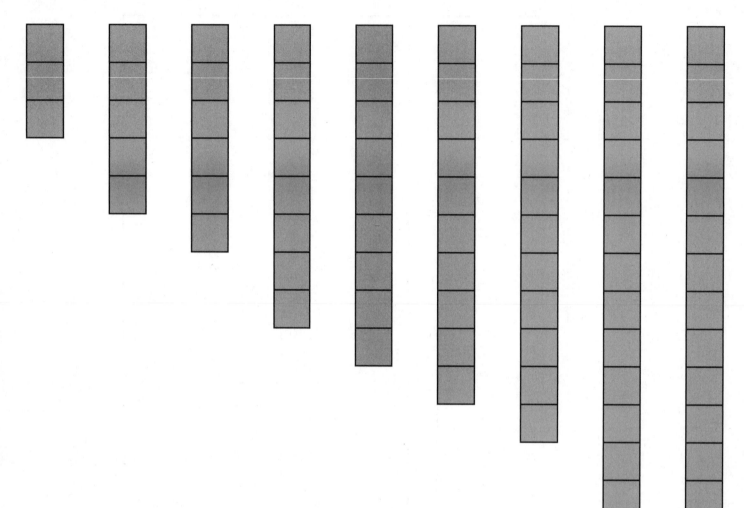

Name _____

Shape Cover-Up Game Board

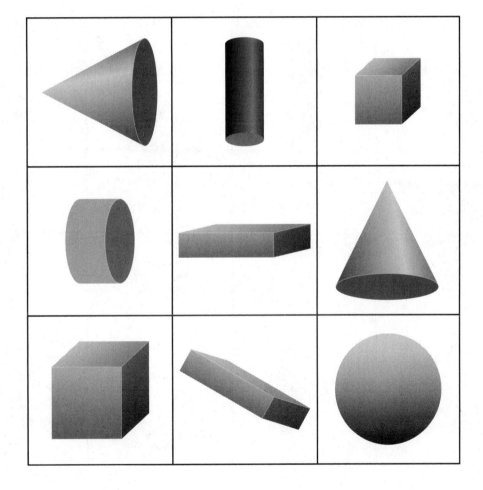

Shape Cards

Name _____

Real-World Shape Cards

Shape Cover-Up Recording Sheet

Flat Shapes	Solid Shapes
Total _____	Total _____